Haskomos Excerpts*

"*Step into My Shoes* skillfully provides a pleasurable way for teens to absorb and implement Torah directed behavior."

"I believe these stories may strongly impact their thinking and behavior, helping them to view others through the lens of kindness and compassion, and become more sensitive to the way their behavior affects others."

Rabbi Yaakov Hopfer
Shearith Israel Congregation, Baltimore
President Vaad HaRabanim, Baltimore

"... an excellent book... teaches tweens and teens about the Torah values as they relate to social interactions with their peers and family members."

"...I was impressed by...how children were not made to feel inadequate or worse for not having the "right" responses to social dilemmas, but rather to look at their middos as a work in progress."

Rabbi Yaakov Horowitz
Dean Yeshiva Darchei Noam, Monsey,
Founder and Director Project Y.E.S.

"...will assist educators to be able to impart Middos Tovos and a positive outlook on life to the young adults they are entrusted with, that will help them through these difficult years and successfully reach the next stages in their lives..."

"...addresses issues which are not generally covered in the curriculum of most schools and should be a welcome addition...to Rabbis, teachers and youth leaders."

The Bostoner Rebbe of Yerushalayim

"...definitely fills a void in understanding issues that a teenager faces. It is something that every concerned person needs to read as it may enhance his/her ability to deal with situations as they arise or to assist others by suggesting proper guidance."

Rabbi Yosef Yitzchok Serebryanski

"We at Bnos Yisroel are excited to be using this book in our Middle School division."

Sara Itzkowtiz
Principal
Bnos Yisroel of Baltimore

Full Haskomos in back of book

Tova NessAiver
Danielle Sarah Storch

STEP INTO *My* SHOES

ISBN 978-0-9991982-1-6

Chapter divider photographs by Shutterstock.com in order of chapters: 1.Ljupco Smokovski, Akura Yochi; 2. Mandy Godbehear; 3. Raisa Kanareva; 4. Paranamir 5.Creatista; 6. Koldunov Alexey.
Story graphic: Igor Yanovskiy

Cover design by Shoshana Radunsky

Simpler versions of some of these stories first appeared in *Binyan* magazine.

Distributed by Feldheim Publishers
Printed in Israel
TODAH Publishing

To my holy teacher, Rabbi Aryeh Nivin, whose lessons and guidance have helped me clarify my purpose in life, and to my wonderful parents, Mr. Lawrence and Dr. Linda Nieman: by raising me in a strong, loving home, you made me what I am.

– DSS

To my incredible husband, whose support is constant and unwavering, and my wonderful children, who hold the mirror to my words and actions, providing a window into the incredible and improbable, making it all possible.

– TN

Contents

Take the "Who Are You?" Quiz

Let's find out how *you* handle situations and what it says about you. What's your style?

After you take the quiz, read the next section to learn about what your answers mean.

1. **Your friend gets a new ten-speed bike for his birthday. It is exactly the one you want, but your parents tell you that you have to save up and buy it yourself. Your reaction:**

    a. You feel happy for your friend (even if a bit envious inside) and ask if you can take the bike for a spin. You are then more determined to save up for a bike of your own.

    b. You think about what jobs you can do to earn money, but feel sad and resentful because it's not fair that your friend got one for free while you have to work for yours.

    c. You complain to your friends that it isn't fair that others should get things for free while you have to work.

    d. You get angry with your parents because you think it is their obligation to give you a bike, without you having to earn it.

2. **A new kid comes to class on the first day of school. The teacher sits her right next to you. The new student can't seem to sit still in class, fidgeting, calling out and even jumping out of her seat. Your reaction:**

   a. You are a bit disturbed, but you figure that she must have some sort of problem, so you just try to accept it.

   b. You tell the teacher that all that fidgeting and calling out is distracting, and you ask to move to another seat.

   c. You tell your friends that you can't stand the new student who is so annoying.

   d. You get upset at the school for placing a "problem student" in your class.

3. **Your cousin, who lives nearby, meets you at your grandmother's house for Shabbos. He is wearing a watch that looks exactly like your favorite watch—the one you just lost. There is even a mark on the band that looks exactly like the mark on yours. Your reaction:**

   a. You say, "Hey, you found my watch. I was looking all over for it. Thanks!"

   b. You ask your cousin why he has your watch and tell him to give it back.

   c. You turn to someone in your family and say, "Look, he took my watch!"

   d. You accuse someone in your family of giving your watch to your cousin.

4. **You oversleep and arrive an hour late to your best friend's birthday bash. Your friend had asked you to be on time. Your reaction:**

a. You quickly apologize and ask your friend's forgiveness for oversleeping and coming late.

b. You say, "Sorry about that," and ask your friend what you can do now to help.

c. You are embarrassed and try to avoid your friend throughout the party.

d. You blame your parents, telling your friend they didn't wake you up on time.

5. The overweight kid in your class finally trims down. Your reaction:

a. You say, "Hey, looking good!"

b. You invite him to join you in your recess sports (basketball, capture the flag, etc.).

c. You and your friends start calling him "string bean."

d. You try offering the kid some nosh to see if he will eat it.

6. Your basketball coach informs you that you're going to be a backup, rather than a full member of the team. Your reaction:

a. You cheer your teammates from the sidelines and hope the coach puts you in a few more of the games.

b. You are disappointed, but you ask your coach if he can help you improve so that you can become a full member.

c. You complain to everyone about the coach because you think he should have made you a full member of the team.

d. You become angry with the coach and quit the team without any discussion.

Sometimes, answering questions like these is hard. Often we know that we should behave in a particular way, but realize that in reality, we probably would not. Try to be honest. Only you will know what your answers are. This way, you can see where you really are and how you can move forward from there.

Let's take a look at what your answers say about your current approach:

If you answered mostly a's:

You are generally a cheerful, easygoing person who looks at things in a positive light. You don't focus on the negative aspects of a situation, don't easily get upset, and accept when things don't go your way. You might think, "Hashem is responsible for what happens to me, so whatever happens is for the good."

When faced with challenging situations, you are able to see the bigger picture, realizing that these bumps in the road are small things that should not affect who you are, your overall pleasant behavior, or the pleasure you take in life.

What you can work on: look to see if there is something you can do to positively affect the situation you face. Ask yourself: "Is this how it has to be, or is there some way I can make it better? *Think:* perhaps this is a challenge Hashem has sent me to see how I can improve things."

If you answered mostly b's:

When faced with a difficult situation, you may feel sad or upset, but it does not stop you from looking for a way to improve the situation. You are a solution seeker. That is a very good trait to have.

What you can work on: don't let things get you down. Realize that everything that happens to you is a challenge you can meet. Know that a better way to handle the situation is there, just waiting for you to discover it.

If you answered mostly c's:

On the positive side, you speak up and say what you think. You are not too timid to take a stand. However, something in your life has led you to feel powerless to change things. You either have not received enough encouragement to think and plan for yourself, or have not received sufficient recognition of your abilities. When something doesn't go your way, you tend to try and get others to agree about how terrible things are, looking for support in your discomfort. While that seems to make you feel less helpless and more powerful, it really doesn't improve things.

What you can work on: instead of looking at things negatively, seek to understand what is happening. Recognize that the challenges you face are there to give you the opportunity to grow by finding a way to deal with them. Use your ability to speak up for yourself, to let others know what you are feeling and how you would like to change things. You might be surprised at how eagerly others support your ideas. Sometimes you will need to pretend that things aren't bothering you so much and just act pleasantly until the negative feelings lessen. Then you can see more clearly what your best course of action might be.

If you answered mostly d's:

You really notice things. That's great! You are aware of what is happening around you and see the details. However, you tend to see the world in a negative light, as if you are not given enough. At this point in life you have not learned to take responsibility for your own actions. Whether it is because you have not been given much responsibility, your parents have excused you from responsibility, or other factors are at play, when things do not go your way you feel powerless and tend to shift the blame onto others. Your sense of powerlessness makes you want to pull others down with you and shift the blame so that you feel a bit better about yourself.

What you can work on: Instead of allowing situations to upset you to the point of not knowing what to do, use your keen ability to observe how others react to similar situations and notice which responses are most effective. See how others take charge and find solutions to problems, and stop yourself from blaming others. Try to think of yourself as someone who supports other people, and notice who or what situation can benefit from your unique help.

To all – a, b, c and d's:

Most of us have responses that are a combination of all four tendencies. At times we are more easygoing and accepting, at times more intolerant of things and willing to shift blame. What we are all here to learn is that Hashem has placed in our path many experiences, each one designed to help us strengthen ourselves as kind, thoughtful and understanding people. We are here to grow as a people who emulate Hashem, who are like Him in the way we think, act and speak. In order to do this, we have to recognize when we are being less than we should be, and find a way to change. Seeing how others handle their challenges can go a long way toward helping us see what is and is not right and good, and where to focus our efforts to improve ourselves.

Realizing that everything that happens is an opportunity to grow—that Hashem has placed this in our path—brings shalom, peace, into our relationships, and our lives.

****

Now that you have taken the quiz and learned a little more about your problem-solving style, let's take a trip into the lives of kids who are faced with all sorts of problems, and see how *they* solve them. We will meet kids who have gone through tough times, exciting times, and even times when they couldn't understand what was happening to them. Kids just like you. We will visit them in their schools, at summer camp and in their homes.

We call this adventure *Step Into My Shoes* because we want to step into the lives and mindset of these kids and get a real feel for what they are experiencing. It will almost be like walking in their shoes for a while, viewing life through their eyes—like *being them*. With the knowledge we have gained about our own tendencies, we can think about how we would handle similar situations and what we can do to improve our reactions and behaviors.

At the end of each chapter, you will meet some really neat people in our *Fun & Facts* sections. You will encounter people such as the lady who didn't speak for 25 hours, and the surgeon who helps people who blush too much. There are also games and activities for you to try, along with some interesting facts, mini-stories, and fascinating bits of advice.

And now, let's take that step...

Chapter One

Your Stuff and My Stuff

Lo Sachmod – לא תחמד

Do Not Covet

Hitting it Home

How does a simple baseball toss between two friends lead to one of them almost stealing?

I love the sound of the bat hitting the ball! I love sliding into home plate! I'm pretty good at baseball, but whether or not I hit that sweet spot usually depends on which bat I use. So I got myself a metal Easton bat. It's a good one, but not as good as the top-of-the-line bats. It was on sale for thirty dollars, exactly the amount of money I had to spend.

My best friend Aaron also loves baseball. Twice a week after school, we meet at my house and practice our batting and pitching. Eventually the other neighborhood boys get out of school and join us.

I'm not as fortunate as Aaron, though. He gets whatever he wants and is able to buy really expensive sports equipment, which helps him be the best player in the neighborhood. I have to save up my allowance and work odd jobs to buy my own stuff.

One Tuesday, Aaron came over to my house after school, carrying a new bat. That's when my troubles began.

"My Dad bought me a DeMarini—a four-hundred-dollar beauty! Wanna see it?"

My eyes opened wide. I couldn't believe it. A DeMarini bat! The one that every kid in my neighborhood dreamed of owning. It was incredible. My fingers itched to hold it. I whistled. "Nice! Real nice!"

"Yeah!" Aaron grinned. "Let's play ball!"

"Can I have a turn with your bat?" I asked.

"Sure." Aaron put his arm around my shoulders, as we walked to the yard. We began to warm up as I pitched, and Aaron hit. When we switched places, I used his bat and hit almost every ball, hitting that sweet spot that sent the ball flying much farther than usual.

"Whoa, you're on a roll!" Aaron called to me.

I knew I would be. With just the right weight and balance, the DeMarini was the best fit for my game.

The neighborhood regulars came by, and we played until kids were called in to dinner.

I looked longingly at the DeMarini, as we packed up. "Hey Aaron," I began. "You know, well, um," I swallowed hard and rushed on, "my birthday's coming up in two months and..." I couldn't say it. I just looked down and threw the ball into my glove.

Aaron caught my hint. "I can't give a $400 birthday gift, but nice try," he chuckled. He ran his hand up and down the bat, a thoughtful expression on his face.

"My dad might occasionally spend his money on nice things for me," Aaron said, "but it's not *my* money." He took a deep breath, squared his shoulders and looked me in the eye. "I get an allowance of $10 a week, and I'm expected to save up for most things. This bat was my birthday gift. And if my dad wasn't nuts about baseball, he never would have spent this much on a gift, even for me." He bit his lip and looked down. "So... sorry," he said a bit sheepishly, shrugging his shoulders.

I laughed and shrugged, like it was no big deal. "No sweat," I said. "I'm saving up and will get one eventually. Gotta get home. See ya!" We each ran off to our homes.

I couldn't get the feel of that bat out of my head. It had felt so good to hit that ball squarely every time. I thought that if I could just have the bat for a while, I might be able to transfer that ability when using my own bat. But...it was Aaron's bat.

That Thursday, after our usual game of baseball, the words just slipped out.

"Can I borrow your bat for a few nights?"

It suddenly got silent between us.

Aaron looked down at the dirt, kicking up tufts with the toe of his Nikes. He was thinking so intently, I could almost hear his thoughts out loud. *Do I really want to lend him my new, expensive bat*?

But what could it hurt for him to lend it to me, I thought, *after all, Aaron's so rich. His dad could buy him any bat in the world.* I bit my fingernail while I waited for my friend to say something. I knew that other kids sometimes asked Aaron for things, and it was hard for him to say no. Aaron looked up at me and then held out the bat.

"Please be careful with it," he said slowly.

"You mean you'll lend me the bat?" I stared at my friend with wonder.

"Sure, but I need it back next week." He gave me his serious look.

"No problem!" I was so excited I could barely get the words out. "I just want to get a handle on hitting the way this bat lets me hit. Thanks a million!" I took the bat carefully, running a hand down its smooth length.

"Okay. Gotta go, see you tomorrow!" Aaron took off for home.

"Thanks Aaron! You're the best!" I called, as he neared the corner. He held up a hand and waved acknowledgement.

I ran home holding the DeMarini with both hands. The sleek wood felt so good, so right—almost as if it belonged to me! I swung the bat around. Wow!

The next Monday, Aaron was absent from school. When I called his house, his mom said he was sick in bed. I called back on Tuesday to see if Aaron was feeling better, and if I should bring back his bat. His Mom told me that Aaron was still sick and couldn't come to the phone. As I hung up, I felt bad for my friend, but thought: *since Aaron is out sick, I guess I can use the bat for a few extra days.*

And boy, did I ever!

I played with Aaron's bat and scored three home runs with the guys on Tuesday and Thursday. I tried calling Aaron Thursday night, but was told he was still too sick to talk. On Friday, I called Aaron's house to wish him a good Shabbos. His housekeeper answered the phone.

"Aaron's in the hospital. He needs an operation," she told me.

"An operation? What's wrong with him?" I had no idea it was so serious. For a moment there was silence, then the housekeeper spoke hesitantly. "The family is keeping it quiet, but I'm sure Aaron would want you to know. He didn't have a stomach virus after all. It turns out he had appendicitis and now he needs surgery to remove his appendix. I have to run now, but I'll tell his mom you called."

"Thank you for letting me know," I said. "Which hospital is he in?" She gave me the particulars and I resolved to go visit him, if I was allowed to. It was hard to picture my friend lying in a hospital bed. *I hope he's okay*, I thought. I decided to say Tehilim (psalms) for a refuah shelaima (complete recovery). But no sooner had I turned around, than my gaze fell on the bat. I hate to admit it, but the thought that ran through my mind was: *Aaron's new DeMarini. Maybe now I could keep it a lot longer.* Then I gave myself a little smack on the head. *Aaron is in the hospital, and all I can think of is his bat? He was probably in a lot of pain. I mean, an operation is serious*!

I couldn't stop thinking about Aaron over Shabbos. Even my mother's special brisket didn't taste the same. But that Sunday when the guys came knocking on my door to play, I went out with my shoulders back, feeling a few inches taller, holding that shiny new bat in my hands. The game started, and when it was my turn, I hit the ball all the way out and scored a home run. I knew that the DeMarini was really meant for me. A crazy thought popped into my head: *Maybe Hashem made Aaron get sick just so I could use the bat a little longer.*

When I got home, I put on my Yankees sweatshirt (Aaron loved the Yankees) and Mom drove us to the hospital. Aaron was lying in bed with his eyes half shut.

"Hey, Aaron."

"Whaaa? Yosef, s'that you?" Aaron seemed way out of it.

"Get better so we can play ball!" I was trying to sound cheerful, but Aaron didn't look so good. His face was very pale and his eyes looked unfocused. An IV tube ran from his hand to a fluid-filled bag on a pole by the bed. He looked weak and...very small.

"Good thing you gave me back my DeMarini." My friend opened his eyes a bit wider, but the look in them was vague. "I held onto it durin' the 'peration...so strong." His eyes closed.

Mom leaned close to Aaron's ear and whispered softly, "I hope you heal quickly, Aaron. We'll all be davening for you. Refuah sheleima!" She turned to me and said, "I think he's asleep again. The medicine he's on keeps him from feeling pain, but it also makes him sleep a lot. Sleep helps him heal. He'll be better before you know it." Then she turned to Aaron's mom and they began to talk.

I looked at Aaron and wondered. Does he think I gave him back his new bat? That's crazy. I mean, I still had it at home. I felt a kind of buzzing inside. "Refuah sheleima, Aaron," I whispered. I had lots of thoughts, bursting to be examined, but instead, forcing myself to focus for a bit longer, I took out my Tehillim and davened for Aaron. Then I went out to the hall for a minute.

If he thought I had given him back the bat already, did that mean I could keep it a lot longer? A part of me wanted to believe that I could keep the DeMarini forever because, with this bat, I was the star of the team. But it wasn't really mine. I didn't want to think about that. In my excitement, all I could think was *DeMarini, DeMarini, I can keep using the DeMarini.*

On the ride home Mom said, "What's with you? You haven't been your talkative self." I shrugged my shoulders. I felt too confused.

"Aaron will get better, you know," my mom tried to reassure me. "Appendicitis is serious, but a young, healthy person like Aaron will be back on his feet in no time. You'll see," she said, giving me a reassuring pat.

"I know, Mom, it's not that, it's just..." I shrugged my shoulders. I couldn't explain what I was feeling to anyone. I didn't really understand it myself. I was too tangled up. I felt excited and terrible at the same time—and my stomach felt tight and quivery. I was deciding to hold on to the bat for as long as Aaron didn't remember I had it. But Mom wasn't fooled.

"It's about that bat, isn't it?" she asked gently. "I know you'll figure out the right thing to do." I wasn't so sure.

On Tuesday, while I sat waiting for the guys to come out to play ball, my mind kept coming up with ways to keep Aaron's bat. *I'm just borrowing it, that's all. I would eventually give it back. Wouldn't I?* And then, the worst possible thought slipped unguarded into my head. *If Aaron didn't...if he got worse and...then the bat* could *be mine.* With a shudder I banished that thought from my head. How did that even get in there*? Aaron is my friend! Stop this!* I felt horrible. Like something really dirty had splashed all over me. As if a war were taking place inside me, pulling me in two directions.

That's when I decided to try my Easton again. It had been lying neglected in my closet. I ran inside, dug it out, and gave a few practice swings. It definitely wasn't the same as the DeMarini, but it still was a pretty nice bat. I knew right then that I really didn't want to keep my friend's property. I had a bat that was good enough for now. If I practiced and got really good with *this* one, then one day when I could afford the DeMarini, I could be out-of-this-world terrific. I put Aaron's bat on my desk and returned to the yard with the Easton.

I didn't hit any homers, but I think I actually *was* a bit more accurate from having practiced with the DeMarini. After the game, I felt better. I went up to my room, walked over to the sleek, white and red DeMarini and made the decision to return it to Aaron on the day he got home from the hospital. I would write him a note thanking him for being such a generous friend.

Aaron came home a few days later, but still had to stay inside and rest. I brought over the DeMarini with the note. When he saw me, Aaron laughed and said, "Boy, I must've been really out of it in the hospital. I thought that you had *already* given my bat back."

"Nope, I didn't. I wanted to give it to you in person, when you got home. I really enjoyed having it, but it's yours."

"Yeah," Aaron sighed. "It means a lot to me, because my Dad really went all out to give it to me, even though at first he and Mom thought it was too expensive." I nodded as he continued. "But Dad said that it was a gift of love and the expense was silly because it shouldn't cost so much for a hunk of plastic, composite or not. But it's a great bat."

"It sure is!" I agreed. "Using it really improved my game. The grip is terrific and the end load is amazing!" Aaron smiled and gave me a high five.

"You know," he went on, "something interesting happened during the operation."

"Yeah? What?" I wondered.

"At one point, I remember a kind of floaty feeling. Not a good one, but like I would just float away and be lost unless I held onto something. I reached out and grabbed and realized I was holding onto the DeMarini. It felt like a kind of anchor. That's why I thought you gave it back to me. It seemed so real."

"Well, it's real enough now," I told him, "and you're really a super friend for lending me something that means so much to you." Aaron smiled a bit bashfully and answered, "Well, friends mean more than things, and I saw how badly you wanted it."

Whew! I wiped a little sweat off my face. It was definitely a relief to give it back. I had come *that* close to taking his bat. Stealing! That's what happens when you start wanting something that's not yours—something that belongs to someone else. It's like being sick inside.

I decided that year that I would mow lawns and do extra jobs to save up for my own DeMarini. Perhaps I could also convince my parents to give me money instead of birthday and Channukah gifts. It might take a few summers to save up, but, when I finally got my bat, I knew I'd feel really good about it, because it would be truly mine.

Best Overnight Camp – Ever

Did you ever go to sleepaway camp for the summer? Gershon's really excited about his first sleepaway camp adventure...until one of his bunkmates leads him on a dangerous path.

One day I overheard my friends talking at recess.

"We had the most awesome camping trip," exclaimed Shimmy to Yosef. "We hiked to a river, swam, and even went fishing! I caught a fish *this big*!" he said, holding his palms about a foot and a half apart. Shimmy was the tallest kid in our class and the one who always beat me in basketball. Yosef, who was short, loved baseball. This year, both Shimmy and Yosef were planning to go to Camp Chaibahem, for the entire summer.

After hearing what they had said about the camp, I knew I just *had* to go to Chaibahem too, and decided to speak to Mom about it.

When I got home from school, I got a real surprise. Mom told me that she thought I was finally responsible enough to go to sleepaway camp, and that she had already spoken to Shimmy's mother and signed me up to be bunkmates with Shimmy and Yosef for the entire summer.

"Wow! That's super! Thanks Mom! It's just what I was going to talk to you about! This is the best! This is going to be an absolutely awesome summer!" I ran to the stairs to go up to my room. Stopped. Ran back to Mom and gave her a quick hug. "You're the best!" I told her and again ran to the stairs and started up, only to stop and run back down to grab my backpack, spin around and run back to the stairs, passing Mom who watched me with a smile on her face. I practically flew up to my room. I didn't know how to contain the happiness inside me. I couldn't wait!

June twenty fourth finally arrived. After a long ride up some steep and winding roads, Yosef, Shimmy, and I gave each other high fives and jumped off the bus at Camp Chaibahem. Groups of counselors with baseball caps and clipboards called out kids' names, and boys formed lines behind them. Yosef and Shimmy were called to join Bunk Gimmel, and soon afterwards I heard my name called as well: "Gershon Schwartz, Bunk Gimmel!" A dark-haired counselor, with a baseball cap and a name tag that read "Benny," pointed to where I should stand. I carried my suitcase over and sat down on the ground as the rest of the bunk was called.

The first two weeks of camp were fantastic. We settled into our cabin with nine other boys. Most of the other guys were from New York and New Jersey, one was from Baltimore, one from Pennsylvania, and one was from Australia. We spent our days playing sports, swimming, boating, hiking, learning, and even practicing archery. In the evenings there was almost always a campfire with singing and nosh.

"Guys, tomorrow we'll be going on our big overnight," said Benny, the head counselor for the older bunks, one day after lunch.

"This is the big camping trip that we wait for every year. Bunks Alef and Beis will be taken up the mountain in a jeep to a closer location, so that their hike is a bit shorter. Bunks Gimmel, Dalet and Hei will be hiking the full eight miles to Lake Natura, where we'll swim, fish and have a picnic. One of the counselors will hike with you for the first five miles. Then, the three older bunks will have a camper selected, who will act as group leader and be in charge the last three miles.

Each bunk will hike on its own, starting out on a different path and meeting the last half-mile up the climb. We trust you to look out for one another. Group leader is a big responsibility: counting heads, making sure everyone drinks, and keeping everyone moving together. I will stay behind to finish up last minute arrangements and then join you at the lake." He paused a second and added, "*I* get to ride up, being in charge and all. No comments from the peanut gallery about being a wimp I hope," his eyes twinkled with humor. We laughed. Benny was the most fit counselor in the place. He could climb a rope using just his hands, and jump and flip over obstacles with ease.

I overheard Chaim whisper to his friend, Ariel, "He better choose *me* to be group leader for Gimmel. I know how to lead hikes! I can do it in my sleep!" He sounded quite bossy. I had noticed that about Chaim from the beginning and tried to steer clear of him. He tended to tell people what they should do and always assumed he was right. I didn't like him.

"I think Chaim wants to be group leader," I whispered to Yaakov. "He doesn't lead, he pushes."

"It wouldn't surprise me if they picked Shimmy," Yosef said with a smile. "I think Benny really likes him because he's so even-tempered."

The next morning, Benny woke us up at sunrise. We dressed, davened and lined up for morning announcements. "Okay, all of you need to make your bunks spotless, get to breakfast, go to your first morning activity and be packed by twelve o'clock. We'll be meeting at the flagpole to begin our hike."

That morning, we quickly packed our bags. Shimmy, who packed in five minutes flat, looked at his watch and kept calling out the minutes, until our hike was to begin.

"Ten minutes left, guys! Come on, let's get going!"

Knapsacks on our backs, the twelve of us dashed out to the flagpole. Other bunks were arriving as well.

"Okay boys," said Benny, "let's move out! It's a five-mile hike to Lake Natura, where we'll set up camp. I need to choose people to carry the extras: tents, a couple of extra canteens of water, and a first aid kit. I'll assign the jobs for each bunk. If you have any problems with my assignment, come to me privately and let me know." Chaim looked at us, as he brushed some dirt off his gray shirt. He gave a high five to Ariel and to two of the other boys, as we waited to hear our job assignments.

When Benny arrived at our bunk, we looked at him expectantly.

"Gershon, you'll carry the first aid kit," Benny surprised me by saying.

"Ariel will carry one extra water, Zack the other one. Efraim will carry the tent, as he appears to be the strongest." Ephraim smiled with satisfaction. "And..." We waited to see who would be chosen for group leader. "Shimmy Katz will be your group leader!"

Some of the boys called "Hey, Shimmy!" and "Cool deal, Shim!" But Chaim's mouth twisted down in a look of disdain. "I don't believe it!" he muttered. "He's not a leader. They're making a big mistake!"

Shimmy, who looked surprised at being chosen, went to stand next to Benny and Simcha, the counselor who would lead the first part of our hike. Benny handed Shimmy the map and a walkie talkie, reminding him to make sure everyone took regular sips from their canteens or water bottles and stayed together on the trail. He turned to the others and cautioned, "If anything happens that requires a decision to be made, you can discuss it among yourselves, but in the end, Simcha, and then Shimmy, get to make the final decisions. What they say goes, no arguments. Got that?" He looked sternly into each camper's eyes and waited until he got a nod from each. "If you run into any problems, use the walkie talkies to contact base camp." "Okay, go!" Simcha told everyone in Bunk Gimmel to line up and follow him, and our hike began.

We hiked through the woods, going steadily uphill along the trail. We clambered and leaped over fallen branches and crunched over brown, dead leaves, singing, telling silly jokes and teasing each other happily. We stopped occasionally and rested, then continued on. It was hard at times, but it also was very satisfying to really push ourselves to complete the hike.

When we got to the five- mile marker, Simcha called a rest halt and said, "Okay guys, you're on your own. Remember, Shimmy is your leader now and what he says goes, right?" He got nods from most of the campers. "Okay, see ya at the campground!" He set off on a side trail and in minutes was out of sight.

"Okay guys, let's move out," Shimmy said a few minutes later. The hike continued as before, and Shimmy added some funny songs, which we picked up from him as we hiked.

We'd been hiking for another hour and a bit when Chaim complained, "When are we going to stop already? Hey, Mr. Hike Leader, can we stop for a rest now?"

Shimmy stopped. "Okay, everyone can put down their packs and take a drink."

Down went ten knapsacks, and out came ten containers of water. At the back, I found a low, thick branch and scooted along it to sit comfortably, feet dangling. It was one of those perfect branches for leaning back against the trunk and putting one's feet up and settling down with a good book. I wished I had one like it in my backyard. I was taking a long sip from my water bottle, when I heard whispering below. One voice got a bit louder.

"Following Shimmy is ridiculous! *I* should have been chosen as leader. Shimmy doesn't know what he's doing." I couldn't believe my ears. It was Chaim speaking to Ariel. He was bad-mouthing my best friend, Shimmy. For just a moment, I wanted to run and tell Shimmy, but I caught myself, because telling Shimmy what Chaim said would be rechilus, (tale bearing), another kind of lashon horah (evil speech/slander). What do I do?

"Listen, Ariel," Chaim spoke a little louder. "I know a shortcut. Follow me, and we'll get to the finish point in a half hour, forty-five minutes tops. If we stay with Mr. Shimmy, our *leader,* it'll take at least another three hours or more!" His voice dripped with jealousy. He stood up and shouldered his backpack. "Come on!" he insisted, stepping off into the woods. "You don't want to stick around with that loser!"

Ariel looked at Chaim, and then back up the path toward where Shimmy was standing. He stood up, hesitated a bit, and then quietly followed Chaim. I jumped down from the log and followed them. I didn't want Shimmy to get in trouble. He was supposed to keep the group together. Maybe I could convince them to stay with the group.

As soon as they entered the brush, Chaim announced, "I am the true leader of the Bunk Gimmel overnight!" His voice rose like a proud flag. "Follow me, and I'll get you to the camping spot before anyone else gets there. Everyone will see that they should have chosen me! This way!" Having just pushed through some branches thick with leaves, I saw him pointing in the direction of a thick wooded area without a trail.

"Chaim! You're making a big mistake!" I called. "Please come back to the group, before you guys get lost and get into trouble!" Chaim stopped. He looked me up and down and sneered. "What are you doing here? No one invited you! But, now that you're here, either follow me and get to the camping grounds ahead of the rest, or go back to the group and follow Shimmy for another three or four hours!" Chaim crossed his arms, his glaring eyes daring me.

I turned back to where the group had been sitting, only to find that they had moved on. Just up ahead the path forked, and I wasn't sure which way the group had gone. Filled with panic, I tried to figure out if I could see which path had more footprints, but the ground was all gravelly and uneven, with no evidence of anyone having passed there. I could still hear Chaim talking to Ariel and realized I had no choice but to follow him.

"Wait! Chaim! I'm coming with you. Hang on a second!" I called, frantic that he, too, would get too far ahead for me to find him.

"Guess you realized who the *real* leader is, huh?" he called. I was able to retrace my steps by following Chaim's voice and soon saw him waiting, arms folded across his chest.

"Good, let's go, troop!" he called, full of self-satisfied cheer, marching off into the underbrush. Chaim walked fast and furious deeper into the woods, with Ariel and me scrambling behind. He never looked back to see if we were keeping up. We hiked for about twenty minutes without saying much. We climbed over a few large rocks and clambered over fallen trees, roots and branches. At one point, I tripped over some prickle bushes that snagged my clothes, painfully scraping my palms on the rocky path, and tearing a small hole in my pants. This was definitely not fun. Chaim never paused, and at that moment, my feelings of dislike became pretty intense. There was nothing I could do, though. I continued on.

Between the brush and trees, I had been catching brief glimpses of a small brook winding its way over to our right. It seemed very peaceful, until, suddenly, Chaim yelped and Ariel screeched, causing me to jump, just as a large scourge of mosquitoes swarmed around us. Ariel and I swatted at the mosquitoes, trying our best to follow Chaim. The sun had gone behind some clouds, and with all those mosquitoes, visibility was pretty low.

"Which way?" Ariel called.

"Just try to go straight, until we get free of these mosquitoes," I answered. After a few moments, we thrust ourselves through a thicket, into a bit of a clearing, past the mosquito swarm. We looked around.

"Where's Chaim?" asked Ariel.

"Dunno. Hey, Chaim, where…"

"Aiieee!" we heard along with a loud crack.

I turned, trying to determine where the sound had come from.

"Chaim!" I yelled. "Where are you?"

"Chaim! Call out so we can find you!" called Ariel.

It was a different-sounding Chaim that finally called out, "I'm here! I hurt my leg!" We went in the direction his voice had come from, and, pushing through two huge tree trunks, came to a sudden drop-off. Looking down, we saw Chaim sitting at the bottom of a ten-foot drop, cradling his foot in his hands.

"I can't stand up. I think I broke my foot." Chaim gasped. "I was too busy running, trying to get past all those mosquitoes to notice that there was a drop-off here. Ow! My foot really hurts!"

"What are we gonna do?" Ariel sounded scared.

It was the first time I ever felt really petrified. What *could* we do? I thought furiously. Splint? Not sure how to do that. Try to move him? No, we'd been told never to move an injured person unless they were in immediate danger. Ice? Ice! I remembered that I was carrying the emergency first aid kit, which had some instant ice in it. Looking around, I saw a way to get down to the bottom. It wasn't really that far, just steep. "Let's go down that way, where the rocks are, and see what we can do to help." Ariel looked where I was pointing and nodded.

"Hang in there, Chaim, we're coming," he called. We made our way carefully down, and then ran over to Chaim.

"Here," I said, taking the instant ice out of the first aid kit and activating it with a squeeze. "Put this on your foot to keep the swelling down. It should help with the pain, too." Chaim took the bag and gingerly placed it on his foot.

"Maybe we can support you on each side, and you can lean on us like a crutch, only walking on one leg," I suggested. "After all, by your calculation, going this way we'll be there in forty minutes or so, and then we can get some help."

"I guess..." Chaim didn't sound too enthusiastic. We tried getting him up on one leg, but the slightest movement had him groaning in pain. "I don't think I can do this," he said. "It hurts too much to move, and I might be making things worse."

"Well, tell me which direction to go in, and I'll go for help," I said. "If we're that close, I won't get lost." Chaim looked down at his foot. "Chaim? Which way?"

"Um...well, I'm not sure. I *thought* I knew which way when we started, but now I'm all turned around." He looked up at me with worry. "I don't know." We all looked at each other, trying to decide what to do.

"I think it's best if we stay together," Ariel said. "That's what Benny said to do, if we ever got lost. Don't move from where you are and..."

"Blow your whistle!" we all finished together.

We took out our whistles, and took turns blowing, as hard as we could.

After a few minutes, Chaim couldn't continue. "I can't do it anymore. I hurt too much. What if they don't find us? I can't wait too long. My ankle is throbbing."

Ariel and I kept blowing our whistles. I could feel a knot forming in my stomach. *How did I get into this mess anyhow? I just wanted to keep the peace.* Other than Chaim's ankle, I wasn't too worried because I knew that sooner or later Shimmy would notice that we were missing.

We waited and blew our whistles. Waited a bit, blew again, and waited some more. Chaim began a steady moaning. Pulling out my pocket siddur with Tehillim, I told Ariel to blow every two minutes, while in between I recited Tehillim out loud...

It seemed like hours (although later we learned it could not have been more than twenty minutes) before we heard a man's voice calling, "Ariel! Chaim! Gershon!"

"Here! We're here! Below the drop-off!!" Ariel and I called. We heard a bit of scuffling and then a man appeared at the top of the drop. He was tall, wearing the tan uniform and wide brimmed hat of the park rangers.

"I see you!" he called down. "Anyone hurt?"

"Chaim hurt his foot. He thinks it might be broken," I called back.

"Just stay right there, I'll get help," he said, raising his cell phone to his ear.

"I found all three of them, Roger. We're at Bear's Den, by the fallen tree." He looked first at Ariel and me, and then down at Chaim. "One is injured, a possible foot fracture, so bring the stretcher and med kit. I'll update you if there is anything else." The man listened for a moment and then ended the call.

"I'm Ranger Joe," he said. "We'll get you guys out of there in a jiffy!" He made his way down the same path Ariel and I had taken. Carefully questioning Chaim, Joe gently lifted his foot and prodded it here and there. "I don't think it's broken, but we'll just immobilize it until help arrives." He took out an ACE bandage, and carefully wrapped Chaim's foot. "Whoever had this instant ice really saved the day. The foot would have been really swollen without it."

"It was in the first-aid kit I was carrying," I told him.

Soon another ranger arrived. He assessed the situation from above and then disappeared for a few minutes. In minutes, a few men came down the side way, holding a stretcher and a case with the medical symbol on it. One took Chaim's blood pressure and the other did something with a needle, and soon Chaim was strapped to the stretcher and the men were carrying him up, one on each end.

"Let's follow him up, boys," said Ranger Joe. "Are you sure neither of you are hurt? I see some blood on your knee," he said pointing to mine.

"I'm fine," I answered, "I just tripped on the path. Nothing serious." Ariel said he was fine, too.

"Well, we'll just wash it and put some antibiotic on it, just in case," Ranger Joe said. "Let's get up to the camp and take care of things."

"How far is the campsite?" Ariel asked.

"Well, if you hike *that way,*" he pointed at a right angle to the way we had been going, "it will take you about two hours to get there. But we have an ATV, an all-terrain vehicle, that we'll give you a ride in, so it will only take about twenty minutes or so."

When we got to the top and walked back to where the Rangers were gathered we saw several ATV's, one with space for a stretcher where they had placed Chaim. He appeared to be sleeping. I guess they gave him something for the pain. We were shown where to sit and soon were off. Ranger Joe rode with us.

"Well, I guess you boys have had quite an adventure!" Ranger Joe smiled. "It probably taught you a thing or two about going off the trail, huh?" Both of us nodded.

When we arrived at the camp, an ambulance stood waiting, lights flashing. We walked over to Chaim as they were unloading him from the ATV. His eyes were open.

"We caused a big commotion, I guess," Chaim said, obviously embarrassed.

"You, young man, will have to go to the hospital by ambulance. Your friends can follow you in my jeep," said the ranger.

"How did you find us?" I asked the ranger, as we drove to the hospital.

"We received an emergency call from your camp—how do you pronounce it, Chay-buy-hem? They said three boys were lost in the woods. We went searching, and we heard your whistle."

I closed my eyes and thanked Hashem for helping us. I said a little prayer for Chaim to have a refuah sheleimah.

When we got to the hospital, we waited in the waiting room while the doctor was seeing Chaim. A nurse came out and took me into a little cubby, washed my scraped knee with some orange stuff and then put antibiotic cream and a bandage on it. It was no big deal. I was too worried about the trouble we would now be in. Back out in the waiting room, I slumped into a chair. A few minutes later, the camp director, Rabbi Spar, came in to wait with us. He didn't say a word, which had me worried. Soon the doctor came out and told us that Chaim's ankle wasn't broken. It was sprained, and he would have to keep it elevated for a while, and then use crutches until it healed. I guessed that Chaim would have to go home for the rest of the summer. We thanked the doctor and he left.

Rabbi Spar looked at Ariel and me and said, "Your bunk returned early from the overnight." He peered at us with a serious expression. "The entire camp has been saying Tehillim for you." The director had gotten the good news from the police that the rangers had found us, and he was sending the camp driver to come pick us up at the hospital. "We are thankful that you are all basically okay. I hope you will think upon this experience, and know that there are reasons for rules. Reasons that are for *your* benefit, not someone else's. When we get back to camp, I will speak with each of you privately, and find out exactly what happened, so that we might try to prevent such an occurrence in the future." He gave us each a reassuring squeeze on the shoulder and left.

When we pulled into camp that night, all the boys, wearing pajamas and carrying flashlights, welcomed us with cheers and loud singing—"Hodu La'Hashem Ki Tov!"

Chaim hobbled on crutches, and we followed him to the dining hall, where we sat with Benny. He told us that we were not in trouble, but that we would have to discuss what had happened and what had gone wrong. The rangers would be back to teach the entire camp some safety lessons.

Shimmy came and sat beside me. "I'm sorry I didn't immediately notice you weren't with us," he said. "I was a bit unsure what the map was showing about the fork in the path and kind of forgot to count heads when we set off. As soon as I realized we were missing you guys, I wanted to turn back, but then remembered the rule, that if we don't have line-of-sight for people behind us, we aren't supposed to go back in case something happened that would put everyone in danger. I did immediately use the walkie talkie to call the camp base and let them know, though." Shimmy looked at me carefully. "You're not mad?"

"Nah," I told him. "I was really scared for a bit, and now I'm just glad to be back safely. It wasn't your fault." Shimmy knew I meant it. We had been friends a long time, and we really understood each other.

Kids kept coming over and telling us they were glad we were okay. At first, Chaim seemed a bit dazed by all the good will that came his way. He acted a bit embarrassed when kids casually came by and told us so. One kid told us, "I sure davened hard for you! Hashem really listened to our tefilos!"

Chaim's parents had agreed to allow Chaim to stay in camp on condition that he didn't try to play sports and stayed off his foot as much as possible.

A few days passed and Chaim came to my bunk. "Can I speak to you for a moment, Gershon?"

"Sure!" I answered.

"I, um, just wanted you to know that, uh, I'm really sorry for how I treated you back there, you know, on the trail. I shouldn't have gone off like that either."

"S'okay," I said, "but I do have a question."

"Yeah?"

"*Why* did you leave the trail? I know you wished you were leader and that you said you had a shortcut, but after all those lectures about staying with the group, why did you think it was okay to leave?" Chaim was quiet for a moment. "I guess I felt I needed to stand out somehow. I never feel like people will like me and think I'm important, unless I'm in charge of things," he admitted. "And then...afterwards, everyone was so nice. They're treating me like a hero and...and...I don't deserve it." He swiped his eyes with his sleeve...

"Maybe you do," I said carefully.

"Huh?" Chaim was confused.

"Well, I've seen how you listen to people since the accident, and you *are* making lots of friends. Changing your attitude is hard. It takes guts. It takes determination. Even when it goes against the grain of what you might usually do. I think that makes you a hero."

"Yeah?" Chaim was hesitant.

"Absolutely!" I affirmed. Chaim smiled. I smiled back.

"We good?" Chaim asked.

"Absolutely," I repeated.

That summer, even though I missed the fantastic overnight at Lake Natura, I learned more than just field survival skills; I learned living skills. Chaim is now one of my best friends. And I thought I would *never* like him.

Well, the truth is, he didn't immediately change from the "I need to be boss" attitude. It took most of the summer for him to realize that he pretty much always tried to get kids to notice him by trying to take charge. A week after the accident, he slowly slid back into his old ways. But, when he noticed me wince or when I just gave him a *look,* he usually backed off. I now try really hard never to let myself feel anything close to hate toward a person. You never know how that person might turn around and show you the good in them. And it's great to realize that Hashem really is watching over us, and that He is the one in control. It turned out to be the very best overnight camp experience—ever.

My Siddur, Our Siddur

Breindy and Shaindy are sisters. Can they stay close, when only one can inherit their grandmother's precious siddur?

Two weeks after Bubbie's levayah (funeral), Mommy sat at our round kitchen table, scribbling lists. I went to give her a hug and glanced down at the page she was writing on. Next to my name, she had written *siddur.* Next to my twelve-year-old sister's name, Breindy, she had written *glass kiddush cup.* Next to my seven-year-old brother's name, Hersh, she had written *toolbox*, and next to my two-and-a-half-year-old sister's name, Nechamah, she had written *coin purse—now, (save pearl necklace for bas mitzvah).*

Since Mommy was an only child, Mommy and Tatty had inherited the rest of Bubbie's belongings. Apparently Bubbie had wanted to pass her siddur along to a grandchild.

"I get the siddur?" I asked my Mommy with awe. "The one her Zaidy (grandfather) davened from? For me?" Mommy nodded and smiled up at me.

"I think it would be something you would cherish and daven from with great kavanah," she told me. "So, since she didn't exactly say *which* of the children should have it, I think it should belong to you." I smiled a teary smile and hugged my mother tightly. I felt so special. Later, I also felt a bit worried. I didn't always have the right focus when I davened. Sometimes I was in a rush and zipped through so that I could go out with friends, or rush to class. Was I *worthy* of such a siddur? But it meant so much to me, and I just *knew* that having Bubbie's siddur would help my davening.

The next day, my mother gathered us together and spoke of Bubbie, and how each of us would have something special from her. She began by handing Nechamah one of Bubbie's coin purses, with some fancy handkerchiefs inside. It was funny to see her eyes open wide, and her big, goofy grin, as she snapped the purse open and shut, open and shut, loving it as if it were a great treasure. She took out the handkerchief that had flowers embroidered on the edges and put it on her head.

"Look! My pretty!" she exclaimed. We all laughed.

Next, Mommy handed Breindy the beautiful, hand blown glass and silver cup that Zaidy and Bubbie had used for Kiddush.

"I think you will love this cup," Mommy told her. "Your Zaidy had it specially made by a glass blower and silversmith who was a Holocaust survivor and did amazing work. After Zaidy passed away Bubbie continued to use it for Kiddush. She told me that the swirling colors in the glass made her think of Hashem's creation, while the soft blue at the base made her think of the menucha, the calmness and tranquility, of Shabbos.

And look how beautifully the silver leaves and grapes wrap around the stem and base.

Shaindy took the cup and held it up. The light from the overhead fixture hit it just right, making all those wonderful colors seem to glow. Shaindy stared at it. What was she thinking? She didn't say a word. Next, Mommy handed me the siddur.

"Great-Zaidy's siddur!" I breathed softly, caressing the worn brown-leather cover. I opened the siddur and looked at the faded, tear-stained pages. I noticed that the cover was the original that Zaidy had used, even though it was taped up and held together with a rubber band. I stroked the cover reverently. This holy book was really mine.

Bubbie's siddur had been passed down from her father, a great Rav in White Russia, Belarus. Bubbie used to tell us stories of how he davened from it.

I could almost hear her soft voice: "And one day when the Cossacks obliterated a town close to where Zaidy lived, he heard the commotion and hid in a shed. He locked himself in for over six hours, and, facing east, poured out many tears while davening from this siddur, crying for Hashem's help. His town was spared."

How many times had we heard that story? And now I was holding that very siddur in my hands.

For the next few days, each time I davened, I felt so special—as if my Great-Zaidy was right beside me when I davened, helping me concentrate. On Sunday, after I davened shacharis (morning prayers), I looked up to see my little sister standing near the sofa, holding her little coin purse open on both palms and swaying back and forth with her eyes closed.

"Nechamah, what are you doing?" I asked her. She opened her eyes wide.

"I dabenin'" she told me seriously, "I dabenin' with Bubbie special thing." I almost laughed, but held myself back. She closed her little purse and held it against her chest...just like I was holding my siddur. What she said made me think. Was it the siddur that was special, or what I thought about it that *made* it special?

"Know what, Chamke?" I said putting my arms around her and giving her a big hug.

"What?" she asked.

"*You're* special!" Nechamah giggled and hugged me back. I felt light and free, and skipped toward the stairs to put my siddur back in my room.

A few days after I received the siddur, I heard my sister Breindy at the top of the stairs talking with Mommy. "I can't believe that Bubbie would leave her special siddur to Shaindy," she wailed. "It's just not fair! Why does she always get better things than I do?"

I quietly ran to my room and pressed the siddu*r* to my heart. I began to daven to Hashem to help me deal with my sister's feelings about me. I wasn't even sure what they were. Anger? Jealousy? We usually got along really well, but what I heard in her voice sounded like something she might have felt for a long time. Did she hate me? Did she really think I always got better things than her?

"Please help me figure this out, Hashem," I davened.

My tefillo*s* were interrupted by a loud bang on my door. It jerked open, and there stood Breindy, eyes narrowed in a sinister way. She just stared, then slammed the door shut.

It's not my fault that Mommy decided to give the siddur to me, I thought. *Why is Breindy so upset?*

I heard the soft murmur of Mommy's voice talking to Breindy, then a sentence that was clear, "The glass cup has a beautiful and meaningful history as well..."

"I don't care!" Breindy's voice rose. "I just had my bas mitzvah. The siddur should be mine!"

About a month or so passed, and things seemed to settle down. I figured that she had gotten over the siddur issue, but I was completely wrong. It was a hot summer night, and Esty, my sister's best friend, had come over for dinner. Our corn on the cob was cooking, and its sweet smell mingled mouthwateringly with that of grilled chicken, the tantalizing odors wafting up the stairs to where we were all hanging out in a circle on the floor, playing Rummy.

Breindy got a few matches, but, for once, I was really beating her. I didn't think much about her being more quiet than usual. I just figured she was getting tired. Nechamah was busy setting up her little kitchen set and "cooking." Every so often she came over to offer one of us some of her "food," asking us to "ta-sed it, is good!" Esty, Hersh and I kept making jokes and laughing, getting sillier with each one.

"We know why the chicken crossed the road, but do you know why the dog did?" I raised my eyebrows at Breindy. She turned away from me and shrugged.

"To get to the *barking* lot?" Hersh quipped, laughing.

I giggled, "To bury his bone...but *why* did he want to bury it?" I paused dramatically, "'Cause you can't bury things in trees!" We were all giggling uncontrollably.

"*I* puts da acorns inna tree," Nechamah offered. "Inna hole. Dog too!"

We laughed harder.

"Sure, Nechamah. But that hole is up where your eyes are. The dog would have to stand on his back legs to reach. If he could do that, maybe he could put it in your tree. He'd sure be wagging his tail!"

"And…and…" Esty tried to control her laughter to add one more silliness. "And why do dogs wag their tails? "I tried to hold my breath to calm the laughter. Esty looked at me questioningly. "'Cause no one else will do it for them!" she burst out, sending us into more gales of laughter.

Breindy looked from one of us to the other, a look of mock disgust on her face.

"My sister thinks she's a big shot because she got our Bubbie's prize inheritance." I could see Breindy's nostrils flare and her mouth pinch tight. "She probably doesn't realize that Bubbie really meant for *me* to have the siddur."

I sat there stunned. Where did that come from? It was so mean to say that right in front of her friend. And what was she talking about?

I stared at her a moment, then looked at Esty.

"I gotta go, sorry," I told her. I quickly put down my cards and ran up to my room. I opened the siddur and began to carefully turn the pages. Suddenly, I heard a knock. Thinking it might be Breindy, I thrust the siddur deep into my nightstand drawer.

"I have something to show you, sis." My sister's voice now sounded bubbly.

I opened the door just a crack, and Breindy thrust a folded, somewhat crumply piece of paper into my hand. "Here, Mommy found this last night. She told me she was going to talk to you today."

What was she giving me? I opened the paper and saw that it was a handwritten note on Bubbie's stationery. It said: "Dear Breindy, *mazel tov* on your bas mitzvah. Use my Zaidy's siddur in good health. Love, Bubbie." The handwriting was scribbled, and the date was a year and a half ago.

My sister pushed the door fully open. "See, I knew that siddur was supposed to be mine!"

I wondered if the note was real, or if Breindy had forged it. I ran out of my room in search of Mommy. When I finally found her doing laundry in the basement, I showed her the note.

"What's this, Mommy?" My hand shook as I held up the note.

Mommy sighed. "I was going to show it to you today, Shaindeleh." Mommy's eyes met my foggy gaze. "This morning I was cleaning out more of Bubbie's things, and I came upon this note tucked away in her jewelry box." Mommy placed her hand gently on my shoulder. I felt like someone had punched me in the stomach. Tears suddenly slid from my eyes. "We didn't know before, whom Bubbie intended the siddur for, so I thought that you should have it."

"You mean, my siddur really belongs to Breindy?" I stood in total disbelief.

"Yes," Mommy nodded. "That's what Bubbie wanted. I'm sorry, sweetheart. We didn't have any idea before that she had decided Breindy should have it. It's amazing that I even found that note. I know this is very upsetting to you." Mommy put her arms around me and held me for a few moments. She drew back, and placed a hand on either side of my face, holding me gently and looking into my eyes.

"You know, Shaindy, if Bubbie wanted Breindy to have the siddur, she must have had a good reason. She was a wise and thoughtful woman. Perhaps you can try and think of what some of those reasons might be?"

On some level, I knew that what Mommy was suggesting was a good thing. But right at that moment, I could only feel stunned and hurt. After about a minute, I felt my legs move. They ran and ran, past Nechamah, now helping Mommy fold socks, up the basement steps, down the hallway, up the stairs to the second floor, and through my bedroom door. I fell face-first onto my bed. Reaching over to my night table, I opened the drawer and clutched the siddur tightly in my hands. So many wild thoughts raced through my head. *Maybe I'll hide the siddur…or put it in a cookie tin and bury it. I could spill water all over it and ruin it so that Breindy never gets it. EVER.* Tears running from my tightly shut eyes, I curled up protectively around the siddur.

Then a strange thing happened. I suddenly felt dizzy, and my body became light, like it was floating. The room seemed dimmer, and I heard a voice talking to me. "Sheindeleh, you are such a special girl. You don't need this siddur; you are already so connected to Hashem and His mitzvos." Where was that voice coming from? It sounded exactly like Bubbie. It was exactly the way she would talk. "*Sheifaleh,*" I heard, "I want Breindy to be connected like you are. That's why I left the siddur to her. It will help her find her connection." The voice drifted off. Was it Bubbie? Maybe. Or maybe I was hearing my own inner voice—the part of me that knows the truth. I sat up and looked around. Of course, no one was there.

Just then, the doorknob turned, and my door inched open a bit at a time until I could just make out a little hand.

"Nechamah?" I called gently, "Is that you?" Nechamah pushed open the door and walked over to the bed.

"Here, Shaindy, you can use my special Bubbie thing for dabenin'." She held out the coin purse. "Good dabenin'!" she nodded her head positively.

I took the purse and looked at my sweet, wise sister. Yes, it wasn't the *thing* that made "good davening."

"Thank you for sharing with me, Nechamah," I told her. "You really helped me. You can keep your special thing from Bubbie, but will you let me borrow it sometimes?" Nechamah nodded happily. I took her hand, got up from my bed and took a deep breath.

I knew what I needed to do next.

"Come, Nechamahla, I'll walk you downstairs. I think *I* need to share something special just like you did." Together we went downstairs to the kitchen where my sister, Hersh and Mommy were starting dinner preparations.

"Here, Breindy." I looked over at Mommy. "Bubbie wanted you to have the siddur, so here it is."

"Thanks, Shaindy!" Breindy stood up from the counter stool and gave me a strange look. "What happened to you? Why are you okay with this all of a sudden?"

I shrugged. "I was thinking about it, and I realized that if Bubbie left the siddur for you, then it really is yours. I can't keep something that isn't mine and daven from it. Besides," I added with a wink at Nechamah, "it isn't the siddur, but the focus, and I can borrow Nechamah's special thing, whenever I need it for extra kavanah."

"Special thing?" Breindy wondered in confusion. But Nechamah grinned widely. Mommy looked at all of us and just smiled.

"Well, great!" Breindy turned her gaze from me to Mommy to the siddur. After a moment, she said, "You know, I was thinking that when you need to daven and I'm not using it, you could always *borrow* this one. Because, well, it *is* special, and I guess it shouldn't just be me that gets to use it."

"That would be super!" I smiled. Breindy grinned back.

"What about me?" chimed in Hersh. "Can I borrow it to daven?"

"Only if you are super careful with it," Breindy told him, "because it is very old and fragile and if you are rough with it, it will fall all to pieces. We don't want that, do we?"

"Uh uh," answered Hersh solemnly, "I'll be careful. I'll only use it once in a while. Maybe also when I'm bar mitzvah?"

"Sure," Breindy affirmed, "that would work. But please ask me before you use it. Don't just take it, okay?"

"Yep, sure, when I want it," Hersh said absently, his attention back on the cucumbers he had been cutting with a small knife.

"I think Bubbie would be proud of both of you," Mommy said. "After all, we do use a siddur to ask Hashem to bring peace to the world."

"An' me!" piped in Nechamah, "Bubbie proud me!"

"Yes," I agreed, "Nechamah helped me see what is important. I think she has a little of Bubbie's wise way of seeing things."

Mommy lifted an eyebrow, as she studied her youngest, then announced, "I think Hashem is smiling with us right now, because we have real shalom here…the kind that comes from really understanding each other."

We all felt so content, surrounded by care, love and shalom.

Fun & Facts

Lo Sachmod - לא תחמד
Do Not Covet

It's easy to wish we had what someone else has. But when is it wrong?

Our Torah teaches us: lo Sachmod – לא תחמוד – Do not covet. (*Shemos* 20:14)

To *covet* means to want what someone else has so strongly that you devise a way to get it from him.

"Do not covet" is one of the Aseres Hadibros—the Ten Commandments.

Why is it so important? Because coveting leads us to think and act in the wrong way.

First, what others have is *theirs*, and should not be *yours.* Second, it is okay to buy or make a similar thing to what someone else has, but not to take *his.* Even if you get him to agree.

Our thinking should be: It is Hashem who gives us, and everyone else, what we have. If we try and take someone's property, it's like saying that we don't trust that what Hashem has given each of us is the right thing for us.

In his Mishnah Torah, the Rambam writes:

> When you desire a neighbor's object and pressure him heavily until he gives it to you, even if your pressure was friendly and even if you pay handsomely for it, you have violated the prohibition. What you did was wrong.
>
> (Rambam, Mishneh Torah, Hilchos Gezeilah v'Aveidah)

Cool Fact:

Scientists have discovered that certain parts of our brain are activated when we want something that belongs to someone else.

The part of the brain that is activated is called the *anterior cingulate cortex*. Behind our forehead is *the prefrontal cortex*, the part where decision-making, planning and general thinking occurs. The *anterior cingulate cortex* is behind that and is one of the areas where impulse control occurs.

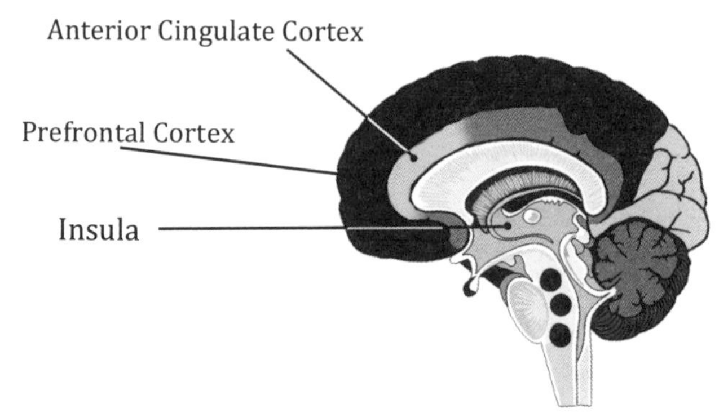

In an experiment, in which people had to decide about whether or not to take items that did not belong to them, participants with lower ability to control their impulses (in other words, people who did what they *wanted* to do, instead of what they *should* do) showed lower activity in the *anterior cingulate cortex and insula*.

True Story: The Rare Siddur

A rebbi from Eretz Yisroel was visiting a talmid (student) of his in America. The talmid showed the rebbi a special siddur that he owned. It was a rare siddur that was not available in most stores, but the talmid had the zechus (privilege) of being able to purchase it. The rebbi was looking at the book and admiring it, when he suddenly stopped, closed his eyes and said out loud, "I hereby declare that I am accepting upon myself the commandment from the Torah to not desire the objects of someone else." The rebbi recognized that he could easily have let himself start wanting that siddur, which would have been an aveira (sin) chas v'shalom (heaven forbid).

(Personal communication with The Stropkover Rebbe, Shlita, January 2015.)

Even though that object was an item of holiness—a siddur—it still would have been an aveira to want it, because it belonged to someone else. By declaring his intention to do the mitzvah of *not* desiring someone else's possession, the rebbi stopped himself from having that desire. When we remind ourselves of Hashem's mitzvos, what Hashem wants us to do, we stop ourselves from giving in to our yetzer hora—the part of us that just does what it feels like without thinking about whether it is right or not.

* * * * * *

Ways to turn away from wanting—To keep Lo Sachmod:

a. Think of a time when you wanted something that belonged to another person. Now write down all of the things in your life that you wouldn't want to give up just to have what that other person has. And think. That person, who has what you wish for, might very well be wishing for what *you* have. For example, you might have a rich friend who is an only child. While you might look at the nice things he has, he might be lonely and wishing for a brother or sister—like you have, that he could spend time with. He might not have your terrific Dad or Mom, or Bubbie or Zeidi. He might not have some talent you have, like a gift for music, math, art or sports. Be satisfied with what you have, because Hashem gives us exactly what we need.

b. Make a list of ten things for which you are thankful.

Game:
At the Shabbos table, play *Hakaras Hatov Baseball—or Let's Be Thankful Baseball.* One player is "up at bat." In order to hit the ball and land on a base, the player must say one thing for which he or she is grateful. Players remain up at bat until they've shared four different things. This scores them a home run. Players are not allowed to repeat items. Repeating an item is a strikeout, making it the next person's turn to be up at bat.

The more thankful we are for what we have, the less likely we are to feel the jealousy that leads to coveting.

Did You Know:

Dogs show a kind of jealousy too! Researchers have found that when owners pet a toy dog, or someone else's dog, their own dogs try to push themselves between their owners and the other animal or toy. The owner's dogs often try to be more affectionate to win back their owners' attention.

(Keith Wagstaff, NBC News article on Dr. Christine Harris, emotion researcher at UC San Diego)
(http://www.today.com/style/pet-peeves-dogs-really-do-get-jealous-scientists-say)

Chapter Two

Hey, Give Them the Benefit of the Doubt

Dan Lekaf Zechus – דן לכף זכות

Judge Others Favorably

The Trouble with Rivkah

Aviva and Rivkah are stepsisters who have a difficult time living together. Aviva has sadly accepted having a stepsister with whom she'll never get along, judging her stepsister's mean actions as intentionally hurtful and horrible.

I no longer looked forward to Pesach vacation. For the past three years, I ended up having big fights with my stepsister. My mother passed away when I was just a toddler, and my father remarried three years ago, giving me a new Mom, whom I have come to love, and her daughter, Rivkah. I don't know why we don't get along. She is only three years older, and I had looked forward to finally having a sister—someone to share secrets with, talk about everything with—singing, having silly pillow fights, whispering and giggling late into the night. But as soon as she moved into our home, there was friction between us. I tried being friendly, but she seemed to always take everything the wrong way. Now, Rivkah was returning from seminary after a year and a half in Israel, and my stomach was all churned up in anticipation of another period of clashes between us.

As soon as Rivkah stepped foot into the house, she looked at me and demanded, "Here Aviva, take my bag up to my room and put it on my bed—and don't open it!" I looked at our mother and she nodded.

"Rivkah has had a long, tiring flight. We need to be helpful and allow her time to recover from jet lag." I took the bag, but I knew this was just the beginning of a very difficult time.

That night, I tried to engage Rivkah in conversation. " So, what do you like best about seminary?" I asked. "Mom says you really enjoy it. Is it the learning, the friendships, the trips?" Rivkah was sitting on her bed texting. She looked up with a disdainful glare and snapped, "You'll find out when you go. Now, if you don't mind, I'm busy." That pretty much set the scene for the next few days. We spoke to one another only when necessary, and otherwise kept out of each other's way. It was easier than one might think, as everyone was busy getting ready for Pesach and the sedarim. Each of us had our assigned jobs, and any free time, Rivkah spent visiting or talking to friends.

One day during Chol HaMoed, Rivkah came storming into the house.

“Stay away from my friends, Aviva! Keep your nose out of my life.”

While Rivkah was away in Israel, I had joined a drama club and had become quite friendly with a few of her old classmates. I guessed she had been visiting with one of them.

I wanted to tell her that we can all be friends, but I could see that she would not be receptive.

"Can't we just get along this vacation?" I pleaded.

"Get along? With YOU?" she sneered. "I'm supposed to get along with the *cherished princess?"* She stormed from the room.

What was that about? I wondered. *Cherished princess? Me? What?* I realized that there was far more going on here than simple dislike. My stomach hurt, almost like she had punched me. I ran to my room. I definitely didn't understand Rivkah, and I hated having her back in the house. But I also knew that this was something that needed to be dealt with. Should I talk to Mom? I felt tense and quivery, and totally unequipped to figure out what to do. "Help me, Hashem!" I whispered fiercely, "I really do want to get along. I *want* the sister you gave me. I just don't know how to make her like me." I rubbed the wetness from my eyes. I knew that Hashem would show me the way.

"Aviva moved my stuff again!" I heard Rivkah yell the next day from her lavender bedroom at the top of the stairs. "Mom! Aviva went into my room again. My stuff's been *touched!"*

I heard her feet stomping down the stairs and running into the office where Mom worked on her computer. Her voice was strident, but I couldn't quite hear what she was saying. I held my breath in anxious anticipation. Sure enough, I heard Mom calling to me from the bottom of the stairs.

"Aviva, would you please come down here?" I slowly descended to a confrontation I just knew would not go well. Somehow, whenever I tried to tell my new Mom what was going on between Rivkah and me, my words seemed to get all muddled and I couldn't say things clearly. On top of that,

Rivkah seemed to twist things in a way that made her always seem to be in the right and me to be the one causing problems. I think part of the problem was that I was still trying hard to make sure my new mom liked me. I just knew that saying anything negative about her daughter would not be a good idea.

I walked into the office where Rivkah waited with Mom. *Why do I have to tiptoe around the house every time she comes home?*

"Rivkah tells me that you have been in her room and have moved some of her things, Aviva. Is this true?"

"Yes," I began, "but I was just..."

"I told you so!" Rivkah interrupted, "She has no business snooping in my personal stuff. I want her to keep out of my room and stay away from my things!" Mom looked at Rivkah a bit sadly, it seemed to me, but turned to me and said, "We all have a right to our own privacy. If you wish to enter Rivkah's room, you need to knock and get permission. And Rivkah, you don't need to make a federal case of something like this. You can talk to your sister and tell her what your needs are, without coming to me for everything. I'm sure Aviva meant no harm."

"Uh, I...I was only putting the..." I tried. But Mom continued, "Aviva, you should apologize to Rivkah, and the two of you should try to work things out. I know you are still getting to know each other, and with Rivkah away in seminary, you haven't had a lot of time to learn about one another, but take this time to do so. You are both wonderful young ladies, and I cherish you both. Having had time to get to know Aviva, I just know, Rivkahla, that you will come to love her. I'm sure that if you each make an effort, you can become good friends, even sisters." Just then the phone rang and Mom waved us off, a signal that she needed to take this business call.

"I'm sorry for upsetting you Rivkah, but really, I was just putting the fresh pillowcases and sheets Mom had given me..."

"Stop!" interrupted Rivkah, "I really don't care *why* you were in my room. Just stay out!" With that she ran upstairs and slammed her door.

It seemed hopeless. How could I withstand the torture of my stepsister's hateful attitude while she was home for Pesach—not to mention when she came home for good in the summer? I just couldn't live like this. Perhaps I could temporarily move out of the house—go stay with my friend Shana. No, that wouldn't work. Her brothers were home from yeshiva, leaving no extra beds. What about Chani? No, her married siblings were there for Pesach. Everyone had full households for Pesach. Maybe I could suggest that Rivkah move out? No, this was *her* mom. Maybe I could ignore Rivkah for these few weeks and only speak to her when absolutely necessary? Refuse to engage in conversation? I could *try.*

After thinking about it for a while, I came up with a plan. For now, I would use my "count down" method that I used when school got too demanding. Instead of counting the days until vacation, I would count the days until Rivkah left for Israel. Each night, as I counted the Omer and marked it off on my calendar, I would also be counting the days until she left. I would ask Hashem for the strength to withstand whatever meanness she dished out without responding. I would ask Him for patience. But most of all, every night I would daven for a way to make peace between us. I smiled as I thought of my plan, and I ran to grab my calendar and marker. Tonight was the beginning of the second week of the Omer. Only two more weeks to go until Rivkah left. I had a plan and I felt relieved. I hoped I could keep my calm for that long.

"What are you doing?" Rivkah demanded. She must have seen the smile on my face.

I looked up and saw my stepsister standing in the hallway, with the cordless phone in her hand. She had just gotten off a call, and now she was focusing on me. I felt a lump in my throat. Rivkah's eyes narrowed hatefully. "What are you up to?" she demanded. I had just finished drawing a big smiley face on the day Rivkah was scheduled to leave. I wondered if she'd seen it. "Um, I'm counting the Omer. Did you count tonight?" I asked her. She stared at me a moment, but finally just said "whatever," and did an about-face, starting to call another friend.

That night, as we all sat around the table eating our turkey cutlets, baked potatoes and grilled vegetables, Dad related an interesting shiur (Torah lesson) he had attended. When he paused to take a sip of water, Rivkah suddenly blurted: "Everyone, I have an announcement to make!"

Dad looked at her in surprise. "What's that?"

Mom's eyebrows rose, and Rivkah looked straight at me.

"I've decided I would like to stay home and not return to seminary." She cleared her throat and looked at Mom.

Silence.

"I know it was expensive to send me, but I really don't want to go back. I can go to seminary here, for the rest of the year, can't I?" Rivkah saw Mom and Dad exchange a silent look. "It's okay, isn't it?"

Mom was the first to speak. "Why don't you want to return? Did something happen?"

"I just don't want to be so far away any longer," she said, not meeting anyone's eyes. We could all tell that something was wrong. Something more than not wanting to be away.

"Didn't you like seminary in Israel?" I asked.

"You wouldn't understand!" Rivkah snapped. "It's not about *liking seminary*. It's about being away from…for… oh! Why does it have to be so hard! Why can't you just let me stay? It's my home too." She looked at me. "And she's *my* mom!" And with that, she ran out of the room and up the stairs.

We all looked at each other for a moment. Then Mom said, "I didn't realize things were this bad. I'll give her some time and then go up and talk to her after dinner." Mom turned to me. "Have you noticed that Rivkah hasn't been happy? That she isn't adjusting to this new family?"

I was stunned. Was that the problem? "She's been horrible to me—but I didn't know it was because she thought I took you away from her. I thought she just didn't like me."

My mind drifted off to the past. I envisioned what life must've been like when Rivkah's father passed away. Rivkah was only four at the time, and it must've hurt her tremendously. It had been just her and her Mom for fourteen years. Now here I was, taking away some of that special bond. Her mother was spending time with me, loving me. *I* was the cause of all that hate. I had robbed Rivkah of her mother.

Dad covered my trembling hand with his own big, gentle one. "Don't think that way, Avivale, she doesn't hate you." Dad could always read my expressions so well. "She might resent you a bit, but she will get over that once she realizes what she has gained—a wonderful, loving sister. Right now she just *thinks* she has lost that special relationship she had with her mother. But it's not true. Love isn't like that. Our hearts have an endless capacity to love. The more we love, the more we are *able* to love." He turned toward Mom. "Perhaps this was not the best timing for Rivkah to have gone to Israel. It didn't give us the adjustment time we needed for us to bond as a family."

Mom nodded. "I think you're right. Perhaps keeping her here is more important than finishing the last few months at seminary. It's too bad, because I think she really does love it there. But right now, I will reassure her of my love, and let her know that nothing will ever make her less important to me." She looked at me. "I'm sorry, Aviva. I'll talk to you after I speak with Rivkah." Mom got up and went after Rivkah.

I helped my Dad clean up the dishes. He reminded me that although things might be tough right now, if we keep working for shalom, for peace and understanding, Hashem will help us achieve them. But it was *so* hard.

After finishing the dishes, I ran up to my room. I lay on my bed looking at my calendar. *Rivkah is not leaving. I will have to live with her hate all the time—her justifiable hate. Her Mom* does *love me. I know it.* The feeling of tightness in my chest, that seemed always in the background when Rivkah was around, became unbearable. I didn't know if I could live with this. I closed my eyes and prayed, "Please, Hashem, help me find a way to live with Rivkah. Help her to not hate me so much."

A few minutes later, Mom came into my room shutting the door behind her. "It must be hard for you, hearing Rivkah's harsh words. I guess coming home and seeing you interacting with me so naturally made Rivkah feel left out."

"Hard?" I tilted my head. "Mom, Rivkah treats me horribly every day." I felt tears fall from my eyes and hit my green quilt. "Can't you send her back to Israel?"

Mom put her hand on mine. "Sometimes people lash out in a mean way when they are feeling hurt inside." She leaned closer to me. "And I think I am at fault for not making sure I focused special love on her, when she came back. On the other hand, there might be even more going on here than just this—something about your relationship with her. That is something you will need to find out."

"How?" I wailed. "I can't even talk to her! She shuts me down every time I try."

Mom put her arms around me and rubbed my back. "Try confronting Rivkah about why she's upset with you. Invite her into your room and tell her how *you* feel, and what you wish for in a relationship with her." With a last pat, Mom stood and walked to the door. "Trust in Hashem, and do your best," she smiled. "He'll give you the right words to say."

I thought about Mom's words, and decided to have a serious talk with Rivkah in the morning. What did I have to lose?

The next morning, I woke up to Rivkah's musical laugh on a phone call. As I washed and dressed, I tried to think of how to approach her. What would I say? I decided to just be straightforward. When I heard Rivkah pass my bedroom a few minutes later, I called out, "Rivkah, can we talk?"

"About what?"

"Stuff. C'mon in." I patted my bedspread, and plopped down on the plush surface, motioning her to sit near me.

"Two minutes. I'm on a tight schedule." Rivkah came in, hesitated a minute, and sat gingerly on my bed.

"Listen, we're sisters, right?"

"STEPSISTERS!"

"Yes, but what I really want is to get along with you like a real sister…to be sisters who like each other and share their thoughts, wishes and dreams." I looked up to see her eyes widening.

"And…and every time you come home, you act nasty to me." I sighed, letting a ball of tension out in one breath. My knees shook.

"Who says we can get along, when you have *my* mother and *your* father doting over you all the time?" Rivkah stood up. "You stole my mom from me. She says it isn't so, that she loves me just as much as ever, but I have eyes. She loves you. She loves your dad. That's why I've decided to stay home—so I can secure my place in this family, and make sure it's not all about you." Her lips trembled, and she added in a whisper, "…make sure my mom really does still love me."

Once she opened up, it seemed that she couldn't stop, and a whole world of hurt came pouring out.

"Since my mom married your father, I've been left out." I could see tears welling up in Rivkah's eyes. She rarely cried. "They both love you more than they love me. Mom took you shopping and bought you all new clothes and she took you out to dinner and spent the whole day with you. And your dad never bought me a birthday gift." Rivkah began sobbing. I moved closer to her and rubbed her back.

"Rivkah, Mom took me shopping because Dad has absolutely no clue about girl's clothes and stuff. My things were practically falling apart and totally outdated. Mom took a look at what I was wearing and realized I needed a woman's touch. You have a whole closet full of gorgeous clothes! You didn't need anything, but Mom still came back with a new skirt and sweater for you. She *loves* you! Half of everything she says is about you. 'Did you know my Rivkahle could read when she was only three? Did I tell you that Rivkah was third in her high school for raising money for Chai in her first year?' And then, while you were in seminary, Mom would make something and say, 'Rivkah loves this, or doesn't care for this, or she makes this better than I do.' You are *always* on her mind and in her heart!"

"Really?" Rivkah's voice was soft and hopeful.

"Really! You are very much a part of this family! You should have seen how Dad worried about whether you would like your new room. He supervised the remodeling, and made sure everything was as perfect as he could make it. When Mom told him you had always wished for a loft bed and loved lavender, he insisted on building you a loft and repainting the room, even though he had just painted it a pale yellow. He loves you. He is hoping and waiting for you to love him back. Mom loves you. And I..."

"You hate me. I've been horrible to you." Rivkah sighed.

"No, I don't hate you. Every time you pushed me off or spoke harshly to me, it hurt me. But I don't hate you." Rivkah raised an eyebrow.

"Well, sometimes your sneering tones made feel like giving you a big shove, but that's reaction, not hate. I don't hate you. I *want* to love you, but..."

"Yeah, I've been the sister from your nightmares," she chuckled through her tears.

"Maybe not that bad, but not the sister I always wished for and was hoping you could be."

"You wished for a sister?"

"I've always wanted one. Someone I can talk to about anything and everything. Someone to share secrets with, and maybe, one day, plan weddings with…and," I smiled into her eyes, "even one day trade ideas about raising our children with…or complain to?" I added shyly.

"Oh!" Rivkah breathed. "I thought you resented me for having had a mom, when you didn't. I thought you hated that I had moved into your house and that your dad took your music room and made it into my bedroom. I totally invaded your space."

"Dad was going to put you in my room or redo one of the rooms in the basement. *I'm* the one who suggested the music room, because I wanted my new sister to have a really nice place of her own. My cello fits fine in my room and I usually practice in the living room because Dad and Mom like hearing me play, now that I've improved. But Rivkah, *nothing* about you coming to live here was something I resented. I *loved* knowing you were coming. I just want us to be friends!"

Rivkah sat quietly for a few minutes. "You really mean it? About being sisters? Even after I was so mean to you?"

"Yes and yes and positively yes!" I answered. "I know we have a lot of things to work out. I know we won't always agree on things. We're allowed to argue and stuff. But, mostly, I want to love you and…and…" I couldn't go on. Now *I* was the one with drippy eyes.

Rivkah looked helplessly at me for a moment. Then, it seemed like the sun came out. She smiled, and, miraculously, she opened her arms and wrapped them about me.

“It’s okay,” she said. Then she pulled back and looked into my eyes. “Sisters?”

My body felt light as a feather. “Sisters!” I affirmed.

Blaming Alex

Every year, the eighth-grade boys raise money for a great year-end class trip. When one of their classmates doesn't participate in the fundraising, things get tough.

It was the one-hundredth day of school, and we were looking forward to hearing more about our eighth-grade trip. Each year, the eighth graders would raise money and decide upon the location of the trip. Last year's eighth-grade class collected eight thousand dollars and was able to fly to Los Angeles for three days. The year before that, the class took a bus to New York City and stayed in a hotel for a few nights. Our class really wanted to fly to Houston, Texas, where we would take a tour of the Space Center.

"It's up to you," Rabbi Rappaport said. "You have a small class, so every student counts. You'll all have to work together as a team to earn enough money for a trip to Houston. Avi, how much does your committee figure that we need to make this happen?"

Avi looked up. "Well, we have 18 kids in the class. We can get a group rate of $115 each for the flight, which, with Rebbi and the volunteer, comes to $2,300. Then there is the van rental, food, and tickets for the Space Center. If we book the visit a week in advance we can get the group rate of $10.95 each for the Space Center, which adds up to $219 total. Our hosts, the Birnbaums, are not charging for lodging at their ranch, so we get that free, but we still need an estimated $1000 for food and the van. So, all together, our estimate is that we can squeak by on $3,500."

"Well, there you have it class. You've got to come up with $3,500. Think you can do it?"

"Yes!" "Yeah!" "We can!" came the excited response from our class.

"But remember," Rebbi cautioned, "if you can't raise the funds, the alternate you selected is Philadelphia, also a wonderful trip."

"I already have some ideas!" I enthused, as we all rushed happily from the classroom.

"Me too!" Daniel nodded emphatically. "I really want to go! Texas, here we come! Hey, Baruch?" Daniel looked at me, and I slapped his back. "Right!" I don't think Daniel had ever traveled outside of our hometown. I knew that the thought of traveling far away made him a bit uneasy, but he was still determined. We agreed to meet after school with Chezki, another classmate who lived close by, to make plans.

Chezki, Daniel, and I started doing odd jobs, raking leaves, picking up fallen branches, laying down mulch, even delivering flowers for a local florist. Together, we brought in the first $100. Our classmates also began bringing in the money they had earned. Some guys helped deliver groceries, some babysat, one gave drum lessons. It was slow going, but we were hopeful.

Five months into our efforts, some of the guys began to complain. "Why are we working our tails off, while some others are barely bringing in anything?" one student mumbled.

"Maybe *some* of us will go on this trip and leave *others* behind, because *some people* don't know how to contribute!" another griped in frustration.

Chezki shot Daniel a look. They both looked at me and nodded. We knew we would be discussing this on our way home.

"It really isn't fair," Chezki's glasses slid down his nose as he nodded in emphasis. "We might not reach our goal if everyone doesn't help. And even if we do, the ones who didn't really work at it don't deserve to go."

"And what's up with the new kid, Alex?" Daniel kicked a pebble fiercely. "I haven't seen him handing in any money. And remember how he ignored us when we invited him to help us rake?"

Chezki pushed up his glasses with a knuckle. "Actually, he's handed me one dollar so far."

"It is a bit strange," I mused, "and he always seems to be in a daze when we talk to him."

"I bet he wants to freeload off the rest of us," Daniel grumbled.

"But how do we know he didn't bring in any real money yet?" I wondered, as we neared Daniel's house.

"Because I'm the class treasurer, remember?" Chezki replied. "I didn't want to mention it. You know, lashon hora and stuff. But we need to figure this out. The deadline's almost here, and Alex is the only one who's brought in only one dollar. Some guys haven't brought in a huge amount, but they *are* bringing in a bit every few days, and some have brought in lots more."

"Maybe we can still make it without him?" I wondered.

"But that's not fair at all," Daniel complained. "I quit working if he freeloads."

"Did anyone tell Rabbi Rappaport?" I asked.

"As treasurer, I had to tell him when I gave him the weekly report. He told me that he'd speak to Alex, but maybe he hasn't had the time yet," Chezki told us.

I thought about Alex. He was a quiet kid who spoke with a slight accent, but was able to keep up with the learning fairly well. He always had the right answers in English, too. Alex had joined our school last year, but this year had pretty much kept to himself. He had been absent for two weeks a few months ago, but, since then, had been in school and doing the work, in his own quiet way.

"It doesn't make sense. He's a hard worker," I said, shrugging my shoulders.

The end of the week was the deadline for handing in the funds, in order to make arrangements for the school trip. Rabbi Rappaport entered the classroom with a serious expression on his face. As we sat, ready to open our Gemaras, Rebbi said, "Your class has worked extremely hard to bring in money this year, and I am proud of you."

I raised my eyebrows at Chezki, and he shrugged. Would we make Houston?

"The total you have raised is two thousand, four hundred and sixty-seven dollars..." Rebbi cleared his throat, "and twenty-three cents." Someone giggled. "That is an amazing accomplishment and you should all be proud of your efforts. Unfortunately, that is still some eight hundred short of the necessary funds. It looks like this year's trip will be your second choice: Philadelphia." Some of the boys groaned, but Rebbi silenced them with an upraised hand. "I know this is disappointing, and some of you had your hearts set on going to Houston, but I am sure we will have a wonderful time in Philly. The amount you have raised will give us a really nice trip, with dinner in a very good restaurant. When things don't go the way we plan and work for, we know that Hashem has taken us in a different direction. Let's see how we can learn and grow from this experience. Let's look at it as an adventure—not the one that *we* had planned, but the one that Hashem has given us."

I heard some boys mumble things like "uch" and "what happened?" but Rebbi began the lesson, and we couldn't discuss it until the end of class.

After class, I heard a bunch of boys talking. "This teamwork idea stinks."

"I worked so hard for this," Sruly said.

"What're we gonna do?" Eli asked.

"Maybe someone can talk to Alex, because he didn't help out at all."

"That's really mean," I looked at the guys and continued, "and besides, it's also *lashon hora*."

"Well, it's true." Chezki spun around to face the other boys, who leaned forward to listen. "We gave Alex a fair shot at helping to raise money."

"And he's a hard worker in class, so why couldn't he help?" said Dovid.

Sruly added, "Yeah, I brought in almost two hundred bucks, and I had to babysit my pesky brother."

"You know," I said, "even if Alex had brought in a few hundred, we would still be short some six hundred dollars for the Houston trip."

"Yeah, but why should he even get to go to Philadelphia with us? He didn't pitch in," said Eli.

"Hey," said Chezky, "let's send a representative to Rebbi and find out the truth about Alex. Baruch, we nominate you."

"Me?" My voice cracked.

"Either that, or you go to Alex and tell him to cough up some money," Chezki glared at me. "Not that that will get us to Houston, but he needs to give *something* more than a measly one dollar to come on our class trip, right?"

"Okay, I guess." I went to grab my water bottle, while I thought about speaking either to Rabbi Rappaport or directly to Alex.

The next day at lunch, I noticed Alex sitting alone at an otherwise empty table. His shoulders were slumped forward with his arms folded on the table. *I wonder if he feels bad about not bringing in money*, I thought to myself. *I wonder if he even realizes.* I decided to talk with him first. "Hey Alex, what's up?" I had spoken with him only a few times during the year, other than when we had invited him to help rake leaves.

"Not much." He looked down at the table.

"Everything okay?" I asked, sitting down next to him.

He sighed heavily. "No, not really." I suddenly noticed the dark circles under his blue eyes, and realized that what I had thought was aloofness was really sadness.

"What's the matter?" I said softly. "I know you kinda keep things to yourself, but I can see something just isn't right. Come on, you can tell me. Maybe I can help." Alex looked down at his hands, then looked at me as if trying to decide what to say.

"It's not something you can help with. It's complicated. And private." We sat in silence and I thought a bit.

"Well, my mom always tells me that if someone is willing to listen, then sharing your trouble makes it feel lighter, even if they can't actually do something about the problem. It's worked for me. It just feels better." Alex looked at me a moment, then nodded.

"My father is very sick. He's in the hospital. While my mother works or runs errands, I've been taking care of my little sister and babysitting her friend to make some extra money, and we go back and forth to the hospital almost every day." Alex bit his lip as if to hold back from crying. "After I help with cleaning up, I start on my homework. We eat spaghetti or rice and beans almost every night. Some relatives are helping out with some money for food, but we're barely scraping by."

I felt terrible for him. "Wow, you're *really* in a hard place. Why didn't you tell us? We might have been able to help out!"

"I didn't tell anyone, because...well, it's just not something I feel comfortable talking about. I'm not the kind of person who complains. I just do what I have to."

"How long has your father been sick?"

"He got sick around the beginning of the year, right when Rebbi told us about our class trip. I know the guys are angry at me, but..." Alex looked at me with misty eyes and his voice trailed off. "I don't even know if I can go on the class trip anyway."

I was stunned. We had all thought the worst of Alex, accusing him of being a freeloader. Trying to swallow in a suddenly dry mouth, I looked at Alex and said, "I'm really sorry, Alex. Does Rebbi know?"

"No. I've been so overwhelmed, and I didn't know what to say to him." Alex looked down at the table. "Rebbi has been trying to talk to me after school, and he's been calling me, but I've been avoiding him."

"But why?" It seemed crazy to keep all that to oneself.

Alex took a deep, bracing breath. "My family is very proud and very private. My parents would be embarrassed for others to know we are, um, that we aren't able to…" he trailed off and covered his face with is hands.

"I guess I have to talk to Rebbi, but my family really didn't want anyone to know. And maybe…" he looked at me pleadingly, "…maybe you can say something to the guys so they don't treat me like someone who isn't pulling his weight for the class trip? It's hard enough that I have to deal with my father being so sick, but getting dirty looks from the guys is almost unbearable."

I nodded in sympathy and felt horrible. Without knowing anything about him, we had judged Alex negatively, while all along he had been working harder than all of us combined, just to keep his family running.

I told Alex that I'd explain everything to the guys and that he shouldn't worry, he was doing everything he should and even more. I told him we would arrange a davening schedule for his father, and that I was sure Hashem would give his father a refuah sheleima. After thinking a bit, I also told him that I would talk to Rebbi.

"You probably should speak to Rebbi yourself. Do you want me to tell him you'll speak to him after class?" Alex's lips curved up a bit, a little wobbly, but definitely up. I'm pretty sure it was the first time I'd seen him smile all year.

"Okay," he agreed.

I gave him a pat on his shoulder, and as I walked away, I heard a faint "thank you."

I felt sick inside. The guys and I had really been wrong. I was determined to make things right. I would meet with Rebbi and talk to him, and then tell all the guys to meet me in the gym after school.

Later that day, I privately spoke to Rebbi, telling him everything that Alex had shared with me. During class, Rebbi sent Alex to run an errand that would take a few minutes, and he quickly called a meeting with us.

"I know you're disappointed about not going to Houston," Rebbi said with gentle understanding. "You have worked very hard to achieve your goal, but sometimes, when things don't go as we wish, Hashem is pointing us in another direction. Perhaps this is just such an instance. It has come to my attention that some of you feel that there is a particular student in the class who has not been pulling his weight. Some of you might even be blaming him for not having made enough money to pay for the trip."

There was some uncomfortable shuffling and mumbling in the room.

Rebbi smiled. "Exactly. When you're feeling resentful toward someone, it's a good time to stop and realize that you don't know what's behind that other person's behavior and that resentment is something that comes from inside you. If something in your life is not going according to your plan or desires, stop and realize that it's not just *you* who is involved. There is another side to the story. In this case, Alex's side. His father became very sick around the time you decided to go to Houston. While all of you were earning money for the trip, Alex was busy taking care of his sister, helping his mother care for his father *and* working to earn enough to feed his family. He has been carrying a heavy burden, all alone. It is unlikely that he will be able to join us on this trip."

Some of the boys looked stricken, while others kind of slid down in their chairs. I saw Chezki lean his head on his arms.

"We need to apologize to Alex, and we need to see if we can help him," Rebbi continued. "I think all of you boys have learned something important about being dan l'kaf zechus—judging others favorably."

"Maybe we can continue earning money to give to Alex's family," I blurted out.

"Maybe we can say the entire sefer Tehillim for Alex's father, as a zechus (merit) for a refuah sheleimah," another boy suggested.

Rebbi nodded approvingly. "Those are all good ideas, and you can organize Tehillim and talk about what you want to do with the money you raised, but the most immediate focus is to show Alex your support through friendship. You don't have to say anything about his circumstance unless he brings it up. He comes from a very proud family who will probably not accept charity, so just be kind to him. May Hashem grant his father a refuah sheleima and give Alex and his mother and sister the strength to deal with this challenge that is before them."

Later that day, I saw the guys talking with Alex at lunch and inviting him to sit with them. I thought about our trip and realized that the lesson that we had all learned—about the importance of judging others favorably—was more important than any lesson we could learn on any class trip, no matter where we went.

Forgiving Aliza

The seventh-grade classes have a rule: when giving a party, girls must invite everyone in their class whenever they intend to invite more than five. So when Aliza sends out invitations to her birthday party, why was Shulamis left out?

I*'ll never forgive Aliza Cohen, not if it's the last thing I do,* I thought. *No way. She hurt me too badly, and that's it!*

How could she be so mean? In our small class of twelve, we all know each other pretty well. We've been in school together since kindergarten, and we all live within a few miles of each other. Aliza is the most confident girl in our class. Everyone crowds around her at recess. Yes, she's the best at playing machanayim, but that doesn't explain it. There's just something about her that draws people to her. Sure, Aliza wears cute headbands and always seems to be smiling, often laughing with a happy trill that makes you want to laugh as well. Yet, her friend, Naomi, also has a happy personality and wears her hair in cool styles, but, somehow, she isn't the one other girls are drawn to.

Last summer, Aliza and I attended the same day camp. We got along well, and often shared snacks that we had brought from home. So, this year, when Aliza didn't invite me to her birthday party, I was bewildered and hurt.

"Are you going to Aliza's party?" Tova asked me.

"No, I think I'll be away with my parents," I quickly improvised. As far as I knew, the entire class had been invited to the party, including my closest friends, Chava, Rina, Sarah, and Elisheva. I didn't want the others to know. I was embarrassed. If they knew, I was sure they would think I had done something bad to Aliza, or even worse, that I just wasn't someone worth having at a party. A nobody. An undesirable. A loser.

"What are you going to give Aliza?" Chava asked me at recess one day.

"I don't know," I shrugged, then dodged with "what're you getting?" I felt a lump in my throat, as Chava went on to tell me her ideas for a gift.

"What do you think?" Chava asked. "The purse or the art set?"

"I...I...I think tha-a-uk" My voice came out all scratchy, and when I tried to continue, I started to cough. "Water!" I gasped, pointing to the school, and running off to the water fountain. From the corner of my eye, I saw Chava looking at me with concern. My eyes filled with wetness, and I wiped at them furiously. I just couldn't tell Chava the truth. My mind was racing: Why was I the only one Aliza had left out? What could I have done to make her dislike me so? Could it be because I said she was hogging the ball, when we were playing machanayim? No, she couldn't be *that* sensitive. Or perhaps it was because of the time she tripped on my backpack and got a bloody elbow. But would she really hold that against me? I kept racking my brain for an answer, but nothing reasonable came to mind. I was miserable.

The next day in school, Aliza was at her locker, only a few feet away from mine. She slammed her locker door shut and passed me in the hallway, without even looking my way. I felt like opening her locker and throwing her books on the floor. Like ripping the pages out of her notebooks and tearing them into tiny, itty-bitty pieces. Like… *Wait. This isn't like me. I stopped myself cold. I'm NOT that kind of person, and I'm definitely NOT going to let her meanness turn me into someone I'm not.* I took a steadying breath and walked past her locker toward class—with just a little twinge of a desire to kick my foot into it. I sighed and walked on. Irrational impulses squelched, I still felt bad.

Later on, in math class, Mrs. Berman paired up the girls to work on some newly designed packets, geared toward improving our math skills. Out of all the possible students, Mrs. Berman paired me with…you guessed it, Aliza. If this was a test from Hashem, I thought, it sure was a tough one for me.

"Hi Shulamis, wanna start from the back of the packet or from the first page?" Aliza asked pleasantly, as if nothing was wrong between us. I couldn't believe it. She was looking right at me, but her usual confidence seemed a bit off. Was she regretting not having invited me? Was she embarrassed at having to face me, when she knew I was the only one she *didn't invite?*

"Hey, Shulamis," Aliza shook my arm, "do you want to start at the back? I think it would be more interesting."

"I guess so," I shrugged and took out my pencil. We began to do our math packet. It wasn't easy sitting there next to Aliza. I mean, how do you sit next to a girl who invites the whole class but you to her party and pretend everything is normal? But I knew I had to get my work done. Besides being popular, Aliza was very smart. She understood math even better than I did. I figured, let me just focus on the work. I'll just think of her as an asset to figure out the math and nothing else. That seemed to help. I was able to work with her and complete the assignment.

"You and I are awesome!" Aliza smiled, as we finished page 10 of the packet. I looked around to see that the other pairs of girls were still working quietly. *How can she be so nice to me in class and not invite me to her party?*

"Thanks," I said without a smile. I turned my chair to face away from her, but she gave no indication that she got the hint.

The next day, in Chumash, our class began preparing for the Yomim Noraim. Rosh Hashanah was two weeks away.

"We'll continue our unit on the halachos of bein adam lachaveiro (the laws of how one should treat his fellow)," Mrs. Kravitz told us. "This lesson will focus on the middah of being dan l'kaf zechus, or judging others favorably." She paused. "Let me tell you a story about a girl named Penina and her favorite navy jacket. She loved wearing it and had even pinned a unique, bow-shaped pin to the front right collar. One day, the jacket went missing, and Penina was very upset. She asked her siblings to help her look for it. They all searched for her jacket, but no one could find it anywhere. The next week in school, Penina noticed another girl wearing her jacket. Penina looked around to see if any of her classmates would say something, but they didn't seem to notice. How could they miss that bow-pin on the collar? Penina was sure her schoolmate had stolen it. She was really upset. Why would a nice girl from school commit such a horrible aveirah? That day, whenever Penina saw the girl in the hallway, she would turn her gaze away. Her feelings of resentment soon grew to a seething anger." Our teacher looked around the room.

My chest felt heavy, making it hard to breathe. Mrs. Berman continued her story. "When Penina got home from school, her cleaning lady, Grisalda, was cleaning her room. Penina asked Grisalda if she had seen her navy jacket. Grisalda told her that last week she had been cleaning up and had placed the jacket on top of a pile of other clothes lying on the floor, in the corner of Penina's room. At that moment Penina's mom peeked into the room. 'Are you talking about that pile of clothes on the floor last week? Those are the clothes I pulled from your closet that you grew out of. I bagged them and dropped them off at the thrift shop.' She hadn't noticed that Penina's jacket had been put on the pile. Penina now understood how her jacket had ended up on the girl in her class."

Chavah raised her hand. "So what did Penina do?"

Mrs. Berman answered, "As you can imagine, Penina felt terrible about wrongly judging the other girl in her class. Although she missed her jacket, she knew that she had to let it go, that it now belonged to someone else. Maybe even someone who needed it more than she did. But most of all, Penina realized that she had to really work on judging others favorably, to exercise the middah of being dan l'kaf zechus."

"But, how *could* she have been dan l'kaf zechus?" I wondered out loud, leaning forward in my chair. "I mean, it really did seem like someone had taken her coat. The other girl was *wearing* Penina's favorite coat. Penina never gave it away, and she had absolutely no idea how someone else could have gotten it."

"I'm glad you asked," our teacher said with a smile. "First and foremost, Penina should have thought to herself that there *had* to be a reason this girl was wearing her lost jacket. She could then have thought about what some possible reasons might be. Had Penina accidentally left it lying around? Did it get placed in hefker (the ownerless pile), because no one came to claim it? Even if she could not come up with a plausible reason, she still could have accepted that there *was* one, one that wasn't negative—even if she didn't know what it was."

I sat and really thought hard about this story. I began thinking about everything that had happened—how Aliza hadn't invited me, and how I couldn't stand looking at her anymore. I didn't understand my situation; it made no sense to me. But could it be that there was a simple explanation for it? Just before Chumash ended, our teacher assigned us our homework. We had to think of a situation in our lives, where we had not judged someone favorably. We then had to come up with some possibilities that could explain why that situation might have happened. I felt that this assignment was a lesson from Hashem, given at this particular time, especially for me.

That night, I sat down at my desk and came up with a list of possible reasons why Aliza had not invited me.

1. The invitation got lost in the mail. 2. She meant to invite me, but forgot to include my name on her list. 3. We had moved to a different house a year ago, and perhaps Aliza had sent the

invitation to the old address. 4. She transposed a number on the address and it didn't get to the right place.

Once I began thinking, new possibilities kept flowing through my mind. The more reasons I came up with to judge Aliza favorably, the better I felt. I actually believed that my invitation had been sent to the wrong address, and that it never made its way to me. I figured that even if I never found out the real reason, I knew there had to be one. After all, Aliza was a good person, and we had been friends, if not best friends.

That next day in school was one of the best days of my life. When I sat down next to Aliza in math class, I told her how much I liked the polka-dot bow in her hair. She smiled at me, but something was still off. She didn't have her usual sparkle. I no longer held a grudge against Aliza, because I now truly felt that I had misjudged her. I tried to think of what to say to her to make things better between us, but couldn't think of anything.

When we completed the day's math packet, we started putting our books away in our backpacks. "Shulamis," Aliza said softly, "there is something I need to show you. Can you come with me to my locker at recess?" I looked up in question. Aliza's brow was creased in worry. "I know things have been awkward between us, but if you come with me, I think...well, can you just please come?"

"Sure!" I answered with my newly gained confidence, "No problem." As we walked to her locker that afternoon, Aliza stared down at the floor, her shoulders slumped. This was a very different Aliza, from the usual, confident girl I knew. When we got to her locker, Aliza opened its door, and pulled out a small, somewhat mangled blue envelope. She held it out to me. It had my name and address handwritten in fancy script on the front.

"I'm really sorry, Shulamis," she said, her voice ringing with sincerity. "A few nights ago, I went to get a pen from my desk drawer, but it was stuck. I went under the desk to see what the problem was and saw a bit of blue sticking out where the drawer slider is. When I worked it loose, I realized that it was one of the invitations. *Your* invitation. Everyone else already received her invitation a week ago. At first, I couldn't figure out why you had been looking at me so strangely and treating me so coldly. Then, when I found the invitation, I realized that it was probably because you hadn't been invited to my party. But, I was too embarrassed to do anything. I couldn't even look at you because I felt so badly." She peeked up at me uncertainly from below her lashes. "But then, after our lesson in Chumash today, I realized that you probably felt worse than I did. Forgive me?"

"Of course I forgive you!" I told her. "I thought you didn't invite me because you didn't *like* me, or that I had done something to offend you, or…"

"No! You didn't do anything, I just messed up about the invitation!" Aliza interrupted.

"But then when I heard the story about Penina and…" I continued.

"But when we learned today…"Aliza spoke at the same time.

"…about dan l'kaf zechus…" We both ended in chorus, then stopped, looked at one another and laughed.

"Yeah," I said, "that story really got me thinking. I was pretty hurt, and even angry that I was the only one not invited. Until last night, that is, when I started working on possible explanations. But I have to say, a stuck drawer was *not* one of the ones I came up with."

Aliza laughed. "No, I guess that one would be hard to guess at." Her blue eyes looked merrily into mine. "So, will you come to my party? I'm really sorry you had to go through all that hurt and doubting."

"Forget it!" I said. Aliza looked like I had punched her. "I mean, forget the hurt and stuff, silly." I amended. "Of course I'll come to your party!" We both smiled.

"Well, I'm glad that's taken care of. I was feeling sick for days about this," she breathed.

"*You* were feeling sick?! *I* could barely swallow, half the time!" I countered.

"Well, *I* could barely walk down the hall, without worrying that I'd bump into you and see your accusing eyes looking at me—not that you were, just that I *thought* that you might be." Aliza was obviously holding herself back from laughing.

"Well, *I* could barely walk down the hall because I thought *you* would try and avoid *me*," I sputtered.

"Well..." Aliza and I both broke down laughing. Every time we caught the other's eye, we would start, "Well..." and break down all over again.

Fun & Facts

Dan Lkaf Zechus – דן לכף זכות
Judge others favorably

What does judging others favorably really mean?

Our Torah teaches us to: דן לכף זכות—Judge (others) favorably.

In the Torah, parshas Vayikra, after speaking about lashon horah, it says, *"b'tzedek tishpot es amisecha"—"with righteousness you should judge your fellow."* This means you should judge people, based upon knowing all the facts.

Because we mostly do not know all the facts about a person, Chazal, our sages, teach us that we are obligated to judge people favorably—to be "*dan l'kaf zechus.*"

This concept has two aspects to consider:
1. When we see or hear a person doing or saying something that might be questionable, we should **assume that there is a good reason** for what they are doing or saying. One should try to stop himself from forming a negative conclusion about that person and try not to judge at all. Things are often not what they first appear to be.

By judging people, we harm them, because it affects how we act and speak to them.

2. **We also harm ourselves.** We make ourselves feel superior to others by thinking they aren't as good as we are, or that they don't do things *right*. That disconnects us from the kind of person Hashem wants us to be. He wants us to focus on the good, and be kind and compassionate. We can't do that unless we assume that others are doing things the best way they are able to. It is not our place to judge them at all. We are here to help each other.

So, if you see people doing something you think is wrong, or believe that they are behaving badly, remember to stop and think—there is probably a good reason behind their actions. Instead of criticizing, offer to help—without judging.

Remember this:
The Torah teaches us that the way we look at others is the way Hashem looks at us. When we judge someone kindly, Hashem judges us kindly (Gemara *Shabbos* 127b).

Tools to help:
There are lots of techniques we can use to keep ourselves from judging others. One way is to think of yourself as having an inner **STOP** and **GO** button. When you are confronted by a situation where you are tempted to judge another, hit:

STOP --→ from thinking badly of others, and select
GO -----→ to think only good of others.

The more we learn, the better we get at taking control of these inner buttons.

Neat trick: Next time you are tempted to judge someone unfavorably, point your index finger out, like you're blaming someone else. How many fingers point back at you? Three. Always keep in mind that when you point one finger out to blame someone else, three fingers point back to you. This trick can help us remember to judge others favorably!

Game:

Build your dan l'kaf zechus muscle. With one or more friends, see if you can come up with reasons to explain why the following is happening:

1. Your best friend didn't say hello and seems to be ignoring you.
2. Your mother has given dessert to all of your siblings, but none to you.
3. Your class has extra homework, and the other class doesn't.
4. Your friend is using what looks like your football, yet you never gave him permission to use it.
5. Everyone was invited to a boy's bar mitzvah except you.

How will you be judged? Think of a time when you needed others to judge you favorably. Perhaps you had to go into a traif (unkosher) restaurant along the highway, because you desperately needed to use the restroom. Or maybe you yelled at someone in the street—to warn him about an oncoming car.

Perhaps you grabbed a sibling roughly, to stop them from stepping in a deep crack in the sidewalk. What if all someone saw was your rough grab? Wouldn't you want others to judge you in a positive light?

True Story: Every Opportunity

The Berditchever Rebbe, ZT"L, was an expert at judging favorably. Here is a true story about the Rebbe:

It was Tisha B'Av (a day of mourning and fasting, because on that day our Temple was destroyed), and the Rebbe happened to see a non-observant Jewish man eating. The Rebbe came closer and spoke with this man saying, "Oh, you must have forgotten that today is Tisha B'av."

"No, I know, it's Tisha B'av," the man answered.

"Well, then you must not be feeling well," the Rebbe replied. "You don't have to fast if you're unwell and your doctor told you to eat."

"No." the man replied. "I'm feeling fine."

At this, the Berditchever Rebbe looked up to heaven and cried out to Hashem, "It's wonderful, Hashem, look how honest your children Klal Yisroel are. I gave this Jew every opportunity to not tell the truth, but instead, he chose to be honest. How wonderful!"

(Twerski, Rav Abraham Joseph. *Generation to Generation*. New York, NY: Traditional Jewish Press, 1986.)

Something to ponder:
Which is easier? Judging people favorably, or judging people negatively? Why? How does doing each make you feel?

Imagine a world in which everyone judged everyone else unfavorably. No one could live in such a world. Without trusting others, we would have no friends, we could not get married, and we would not be able to do business. Judging others favorably allows us to live and grow together.

Cool Stuff: Optical Illusions
Do you see what I see?

Think:
When we work on being dan l'kaf zechus, we learn that everything might not be as it appears at first glance. This is also the case with optical illusions. Sometimes, things aren't quite what they appear to be, when you take a closer look. Just like the eye can be fooled, so can our perceptions of people and events.

(Note: the following graphics are all public domain and may be found in many books about optical illusions.)

Does the circle move or is it still?

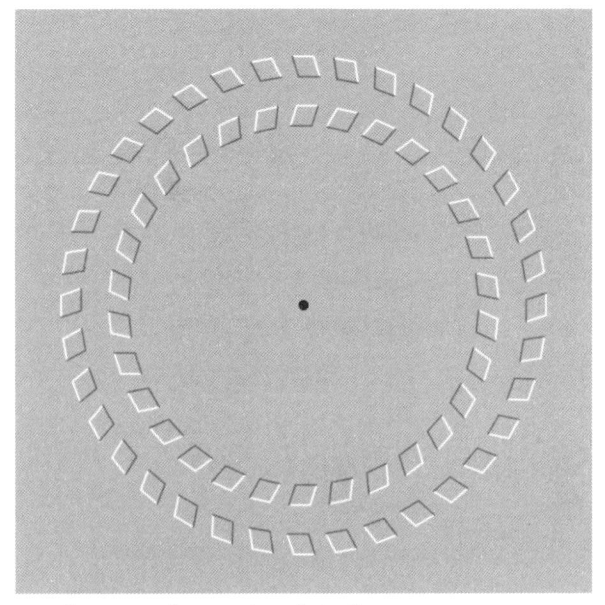

Stare at the center dot, then move your face closer and further from the image

Do you see a rabbit or a duck?

How many black dots do you see? How many white dots? Are they really there?

How many legs does this elephant have?

(Attributed to cognitive scientist Roger N. Shepard)

Do you see a nurse or an old lady? Turn the page upside down and look.

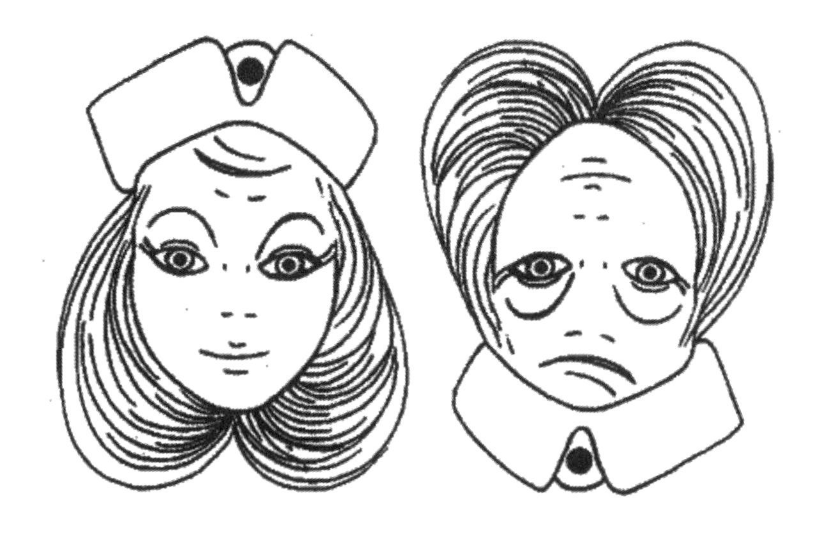

Illusions can be tricky. So can our own first perceptions.

Always remember: Take a second to look more carefully. Even if you don't see the illusion, or don't see why a person is behaving a certain way, assume that what you are seeing might not be quite what you think.

Chapter Three

Save Them from Embarrassment

Halbanas Panim – הלבנת פנים

Embarrassing Others

(Literally: whitening of the face)

Dov-From-Baastin

Dov is new to the school. What happens when kids begin calling him by a nickname he doesn't like?

Shorty. I remember clearly the day my cousin, Ari, began calling me that instead of Ephraim. I had been playing dreidel with Ari and a bunch of my cousins at my grandmother's annual Chanukah party. Usually, it was Ari that won the dreidel contest. He could spin a dreidel upside down for almost two minutes. But that year I had mastered the technique to keep that baby spinning for over two minutes—and I won!

I could see that Ari didn't like that one bit. Instead of high fiving me and slapping me on the back like my other cousins were doing, he looked both amazed and disgruntled, his mouth set in a very unhappy line. Then, right in front of everyone, he blurted, "No way, Shorty! What'd you do? Practice all year so you could beat me?"

"Well, I *did* practice," I admitted, "just for the last few weeks, though." Ari grunted and with a huge sigh let his displeasure go. After all, we *were* cousins and usually the best of friends. It's just hard losing your place as best in something.

"Come on, Shorty, let's all go out and climb Bubbie's climbing tree," he suggested. I guess that once he used that nickname, he liked it and decided he would continue.

"Yeah!" "Great!" "Let's go!" my cousins all agreed. "C'mon Shorty, don't just sit there!" called Elad, giving me a nudge, as I gathered up my dreidel. That was it. From then on, like it or not, I became "Shorty."

It's true that I was short. In fact, over Chol HaMoed Sukkos I hadn't been able to ride the new, backwards swirling rollercoaster at the amusement park, because I was too short. It seemed that I was the only one in the family that got the short gene. All my other cousins were average to tall for their ages. But, being short didn't really bother me too much. I knew that eventually I would grow taller.

The nickname didn't bother me either because I knew that, for the most part, my cousins used it affectionately. We really liked each other. In a way, it was an expression of familiarity and liking. So, "Shorty" it was.

When I got to school after Chanukah break, my best friend, Yehudah, who hadn't even been at my Bubbie's house, greeted me with, "How was Chanukah, Shorty?"

Somehow, he had heard from Ari and the others about my new nickname. That's what happens when all your cousins attend the same school. Since most of us kids called Yehuda, "Yudi," I couldn't complain. Not that I wanted to, really.

Later that day in English class, our teacher told us that we were going to write "letters to a friend." She wrote a sample letter on the board, and we had to choose someone in class to write to.

When our teacher collected the practice letters, she called on Yehudah to read his before the class. He stood up and began:

"January 5, 2014, 3203 Trimble Way, Philadelphia, PA 21145.

"Dear Shorty, I'm so glad that we are best friends. I like playing football with you, and I especially like raking leaves together after school. It's a lot of fun jumping into the big piles we rake up and burying each other in them, particularly since I don't have to work as hard on my pile because it doesn't take as much to cover you up. Would you like to get together this Sunday afternoon?

"Write soon, your friend, Yudi."

When Yudi said "Dear Shorty," the whole class broke out laughing. They also laughed after that crack about not needing to work so hard because I was small. I laughed too, but then it dawned on me. It was official. Shorty was now my nickname. And the nickname stuck. Most of the kids in my class used it, and of course my cousins did too. It made me feel kind of special, as if everyone accepted me and I was one of the guys.

Around that time, I got to know a boy in the other fifth grade, across the hall. His name was Dov. He had just moved to town from Boston and spoke with a funny accent. Sometimes when he was walking down the hall, the boys would tease him and say, “There goes Dov from Baastin.” They said it all at once, as if it were a single word: “DovfromBaastin.” That was how Dov pronounced Boston, with a very long “ah” sound. Occasionally, when Dov passed them in the hall, a boy would call out, “DovfromBaastin!” Mostly, I think, guys just got a kick out of saying the name the way Dov did, with that strong Bostonian accent. They didn’t mean anything bad by saying it. But whenever Dov heard it, he would flinch a little and pull in on himself, tucking his chin down and hurrying away. Some people can’t seem to help picking up on what bothers another and teasing them about it. Those boys would come up behind Dov and quickly stick their mouths close to Dov’s ear and whisper, “DovfromBaastin!” and then run off.

Since Dov had such a different way of pronouncing things, kids just couldn’t help imitating him. Once, when we were out at recess, I heard a kid from Dov’s class saying, “Can’t DovfromBaastin catch?” Guys took every opportunity to say the name. I know it wasn’t because of Dov’s skill level, because he was actually a pretty good catcher. I knew, because some of the kids from my class and I would sometimes play catch with him at recess. When I grabbed my green Eagles football and tossed a fast spiral at him, he smoothly made the grab and tucked it in. He hardly ever fumbled the ball. At least, not until he heard someone shout, “Go for it, DovfromBaastin!” or “Go out for the pass, DovfromBaa-a-a-stin!” Some of those kids were being downright mean, but others just thought it was funny to disrupt someone’s game. Dov would always trip or fumble the ball when he heard them.

"Leave him alone!" I yelled back. "Keep out of our game!" called another of our friends. "Buzz off!" added another. But, although that particular kid might leave, the trend continued.

One day, during recess, a kid from Dov's class tossed him the ball. It shot through the air and spiraled right to where Dov was standing. He held up his hands in the classic triangle to make the catch just as some boys called out, "Run and catch it, DovfromBaastin!" "To the fah end of the yahd!" "Near the cahs!" They broke up laughing. For a split second, Dov froze, his eyes quickly shifting in their direction. That momentary lapse was all it took. The ball struck him smack in the forehead, causing him to fall back and hit his head on the concrete, where he lay unmoving.

Alarmed, a bunch of us ran over to see if we could help. Dov lay motionless, his eyes closed, his face weirdly pale, blood streaming from his scalp. So much blood!

"Dov, we're calling Hatzalah, don't worry," I told him as I crouched down beside him and cautiously took one of his hands. "You're going to be okay." I wasn't sure if I was reassuring him or myself. Betzalel said he would run to get a rebbi to call Hatzalah and took off for the school building. The other boys gathered around in a circle. Dov moaned a bit, but his eyes remained closed and his face was all wobbly, as if all the muscles had gone soft. A rebbi rushed over and felt Dov's pulse, then had us all move back a bit. Before we knew it, Hatzalah was there and Dov was lifted onto a stretcher and whisked off in their ambulance. I felt stunned. Everything had happened so quickly. My breath couldn't quite fill my lungs. Would Dov be okay? I couldn't get the picture of Dov's face out of my thoughts. All that blood and the slackness of his face…it was horrible.

There was still a little bit of recess left, but we all just stood around, unsure how to act, what to do, what to say. Everyone looked shocked, dazed, and worried. A few boys stood looking down at their feet, one kid kicking repeatedly at the loose gravel, venting his feelings through motion.

"Why'd ya throw the ball so hard, Kaplan?" Asher, a tall redhead, accused.

"Me?" said the kid who'd thrown the ball. "Hey, you were the one who yelled 'Run and catch it, DovfromBaastin!'"

"So what?" said Asher. "We always call him DovfromBaastin!"

"Yeah, but not like that," Kaplan told him.

"Like what?" Asher lifted his chin defiantly, "I didn't mean anythin'."

After recess our principal, Rabbi Schwartz, called an assembly for the whole school and led us in Tehillim for Dov ben Rivkah. He explained that Dov had suffered a head injury when he fell, and that the hospital was keeping him there to monitor his condition. Everyone was in shock, still trying to process what had happened.

The next day, we were all pretty quiet in class, without the usual joking and jostling. Dov and his injury were still weighing heavily on everyone's mind. An announcement was made that there would be another assembly after davening to discuss the situation.

On our way to the auditorium, I heard a kid say, "Didn't you see that every time someone called him DovfromBaastin he got upset?"

"What?" a second voice asked. "It's just a nickname. Lots of kids have nicknames."

"Yeah, Shorty doesn't mind his nickname," I heard Asher say. "And I don't mind when kids call me 'Red,' either."

"I know, but I think, maybe, because he's new here, the nickname really got to Dov," Dovid, a short boy with dark brown hair spoke up.

"You guys are way off base," Noam, one of the boys who had teased Dov on the field, loudly interrupted. "You think we made him get hurt? He never complained about his nickname. It was just an accident. He wasn't looking at the ball." He shook his head.

The assembly began with Tehillim. Rabbi Schwartz told us that Dov was being monitored in the hospital for his head injury and that they didn't yet know how serious it was. He asked for boys to take on a mitzvah (good deed) in Dov's merit for a refuah sheleimah. He also suggested that some might learn an extra section of Torah or say Tehillim, or choose a middah (character trait) that they could improve upon. Then he took his hat off, put it on the shtender (lectern) and looked at us with great seriousness. We waited quietly, worried about what was coming next.

"Everything that happens is something that we must learn from," Rabbi Schwartz began. "When one of us is hurt, any of Klal Yisroel, but especially someone in our midst, someone who we know personally, it means we have to examine our ways and see what we might not be doing right, and where we can improve."

"I want those of you who know Dov to think carefully about how you have acted towards him. Have you been friendly?

Have you been kind to someone who is new and unfamiliar with our school and our town? Is there something about your behavior that needs improvement? I am sure that if you look carefully, some of you might find things you need to work on."

Rabbi Schwartz paused to let his words sink in. I felt that he could see right into our neshamas (souls). The room was absolutely silent. I looked over to my right at one of the boys who had teased Dov. He was looking down at his hands, which were clenched tightly on his lap.

"Everything we do affects us and those around us. Let's make sure that we are doing our part to make our school, our community, our people—strong. Strong in kindness, strong in understanding, strong in lending a helpful hand. You are all young men. Don't you want to be strong?"

Kids nodded their heads, a few answering softly, "Yes!"

Rabbi Schwartz nodded back. "Strength isn't just about muscles in your body. The real source of strength is in making the decision to act as you *should,* not as your yetzer hora leads you to act. It might *feel* strong to taunt and tease another. You get to be the powerful one that others are afraid of. It seems like the only way to have value is to make someone feel less than you. But, if you pay close attention to how you really feel *after* taunting someone, you will see that it really leaves you feeling weak and empty. I ask you now, think about it. Is that strength? And is it strength or weakness to stand by and allow someone else to be mistreated—to be bullied?"

Some boys were biting their lips, others shook their heads, some just looked thoughtful. I knew that my face was reflecting the determination I felt inside. I *would not* turn a blind eye to teasing any longer.

"May Hashem grant a refuah sheleima to Dov ben Rivka!" With that, Rabbi Schwartz left the stage and Mr. Schechter, the school guidance counselor, told us to go to second period. As we left the auditorium, some boys were whispering about Dov and what his condition might be. Others returned to their usual chatter, but most seemed more quiet and thoughtful.

When I got to my room, I discovered that both fifth grade classes had been instructed to sit together in one room. Rabbi Rietti told us that he wanted to teach this grade, in particular, about a mitzvah called *halbanas panim*.

Oh, boy, I could see everyone thinking. *Now we're going to get it.* But Rabbi Rietti just leaned on his shtender (lectern) and began, almost casually, "You all have learned a bit about halbanas panim, which is embarrassing or humiliating someone. The words translate as the whitening of the face—which often happens when someone is embarrassed—they get either red in the face or white. Causing someone to feel humiliated is, as you have learned, an aveira, strictly forbidden by the Torah. But, I don't think that many of you know that calling people nicknames that they don't particularly like is also halbanas panim. Even if they accept the nickname, very often, deep inside, they don't like it."

I felt as if Rebbi was looking straight at me, but knew he was looking at everybody. "You should know that according to our mesorah (tradition), one who engages in halbanas panim loses his portion in Olam Habah (the World to Come.) This doesn't mean…"

"CRASH!" Noam's seat fell over as he pushed away from his desk and raced out of the room, a look of horror on his face.

Rabbi Rietti stood and walked calmly after Noam, saying, "Everyone remain in your seats. DO NOT discuss this. I'll be right back. You will experience something now that you might never have a chance to be part of again, and if you let it, it can change your life."

There was shock and excitement on the faces of the other guys. I was pretty shaken myself, feeling a strange mix of dread and worry. I knew why Noam had fled. He was one of the boys who had constantly taunted Dov. Would he really lose his place in Olam Habah? That was really a scary thought.

A few minutes passed in which some of the boys whispered together, but most just sat quietly, some fiddling with their pens or looking at things in their desks. Soon Rebbi came back in with Noam by his side. Noam looked okay, calm and in control. He went back to his seat and Rebbi spoke.

"As I was saying, one who does the aveira of halbanas panim is said to lose his place in Olam Habah. Why do you think this might be so?"

A few boys raised their hands.

"Michoel?" Rebbi nodded.

"I think it's because you don't deserve Olam Habah if you do something to make someone else really feel bad," Michoel suggested.

"Excellent," affirmed Rebbi. "Now let's look at it from the other side. What is Olam Habah?"

"It's the place you go to after you die," called out Baruch.

"It is that," said Rebbi, "but it is also the place you arrive at, when you grow to be a true ben Torah. Think of it as the place you graduate to. How can you graduate, if you haven't done the work and learned what you need to learn, hmmm?"

Wow! I thought. That's a different way of thinking about it. I looked at Noam. What made him look so calm after all that happened?

"Now, I'll tell you a secret," Rebbi continued, "We have lots of consequences in the Torah that we are deserving of when we do something we shouldn't. So, if you do the thing the Torah forbids, do you automatically get that punishment?" The boys looked unsure, but intrigued. Where was this leading?

"Noam?" Rebbi looked at Noam with raised eyebrows, "perhaps you can now answer this?"

Noam took a deep breath and said, "Hashem isn't ever trying to punish us. He just wants us to learn the right way to act. So, if we learn from what we did and change our way of thinking and our behavior, then we not only don't get the punishment, we get a bracha!" Noam finished with a flourish.

"Exactly," confirmed Rebbi. "We are here to learn. Every time we learn from a wrong move we made, and turn to do it the right way, we are doing real teshuva—turning to Hashem's way. Then we get the bracha of doing what is right, what is the Torah way."

I was staring at Noam. He seemed a different person; somehow proud and so much stronger than he had been—in a good way.

"Noam has given me permission to tell you that he left the room with remorse. He now sees what was wrong with his behavior, and knows he will no longer act that way. That makes him a different person. A person worthy of bracha," Rabbi Rietti affirmed.

It was true. He was a different person. We could all see it. It seems such a little thing. And at the same time, such a big thing.

So, let us all gain a bracha from this experience and turn from one of the most hurtful, damaging aveiros between young people, halbanas panim, causing another shame or embarrassment. Let's reach for ways to build each other up, not put them down. Be a cheerleader for your fellow."

Someone wasn't very quiet when he whispered, "Even the creeps?"

Rebbi smiled. "You know, when I was in fifth grade, other kids called me a nerd. I was one of those 'creeps.' You never know how someone will turn out. You can help that 'creep' turn out well by just supporting him and letting him grow into the man he can become. Also, by giving yourself a chance to get to know that 'creep,' you just might find someone worthwhile under the outer objectionable appearance or behavior."

Asher, the boy who had started the teasing, raised his hand. "But, Rebbi, not all nicknames are bad. Like,"—he pointed to me— "Shorty doesn't mind his nickname."

Rabbi Rietti left the shtender. He walked right up to Asher and whispered something in his ear.

Asher stood up and walked over to me. "Ephraim, do you mind being called Shorty?" he said, tilting his head slightly.

The class sat in complete silence as all eyes looked in my direction.

"I don't really mind either way," I answered. But, when I really thought about it, I was no longer so sure.

Rachel's True Performance

One girl has a really good voice—the other needs more practice. What happens when they both audition for the choir?

Ever since the second grade, Rachel and I have dreamed of joining the Shiru Na Girls Choir. You have to be in sixth grade or over to try out, and only those who sing really well make it in. Landing a solo is even more difficult, as your voice has to be perfect, for a particular song.

Hashem blessed my best friend, Rachel, with a beautiful voice. She also has wonderful middos (character traits), using her talent to help others. She volunteers to visit and sing for an elderly lady, once a week, and is the girl that everyone calls to get help with homework. When she sings, it sounds like beautiful birdsong. My voice? It varies. Sometimes it sounds like a recorder, blown a bit too hard—somewhat squeaky and sharp. But, at other times, I've been told it sounds just like a flute. Rachel and I laugh about it, but truth be told, when I really practice, my voice has potential. So my parents hired Ms.

Simon, a fantastic voice coach, to work with me. By the time tryouts rolled around, my voice was much more reliably sweet.

You can imagine how really nervous I was, when the head of Shiru Na told me to sing. I managed a nice version of "Hinei Ma Tov" and was overjoyed when a week later I was accepted into the choir. Of course, Rachel made it as well, and life was just great. We couldn't wait for our first concert, which was going to be held at a local college auditorium later that year.

"I can't wait for the show," Rachel sighed, six months into our practice. "Goldie, are you ready for our solos?"

Oh, I forgot to tell you that both Rachel and I had been given solos as well as a duet to end the concert. I had heard that some of the girls who didn't have solos were a bit jealous of me. I ignored their comments about how my voice cracks when I get nervous and just kept working with Ms. Simon to get ready for my part.

"Sing it more slowly, Goldie," Ms. Simon's gentle voice suggested. "This time, don't try to race through it. Focus on your breathing." I took a deep breath and the words to *Rachem* sang out.

"Better." She said with a smile. "Try it again."

"How do you sing without making mistakes?" I looked up into Ms. Simon's soft, brown eyes. A few months earlier, my sister and I had heard her perform at our school assembly. She had a perfect voice and didn't ever seem to make mistakes.

"I practice until I know I have all the words and melodies down perfectly. Then, when I get up to perform, I don't think about my singing," Ms. Simon closed her eyes a minute and continued, "rather, I put myself into the song." She looked at me thoughtfully. "I think about the meaning of the words I sing, not about *how* I'm singing."

"You don't have a little voice in your head that keeps telling you if you are singing well or not?" I looked at Ms. Simon and thought about all of my little voices that constantly told me that I was either on key or off, too loud, too soft—voices that kept track of my performance, at every moment.

"I got rid of those voices years ago, Goldie," Ms. Simon smiled. "They can ruin a good performance."

"How do I get rid of mine?" I hoped Ms. Simon could help me.

"You've already taken the first step," she said.

"I have?" It was a surprise to me.

"You are aware of them, so now you can choose to listen to them, or to let them go—poof! You forget about them and think of the meaning of the song. That makes the whole way you sing change, with real emotion in the voice that people can hear." Ms. Simon's look said she had confidence in my abilities. At that moment, I thought that I just might be able to do what she said.

"Let's try to apply this to the next song, and see if it helps." Ms. Simon and I talked about the meaning of the next song. She helped me understand it more fully and then had me sing it. I was so focused on *what* I was singing that I forgot to worry about *how* I was sounding. I couldn't believe it. The singing came much more easily, and I didn't sweat as much either. But could I do that at the concert, when I'd be up on stage in front of a crowd of women and girls? I wasn't sure.

That next week, I practiced many times with Rachel, using what I had learned from Ms. Simon. I also practiced singing alone in front of my mirror, while imagining a crowd of people watching me. Sometimes I could hear those inner, annoying voices telling me I was slightly off key, too fast, too uneven, and other times I thought of the beautiful messages in the songs. Singing was so much more fulfilling when I was able to do that. Rachel told me I had improved, and I was excited.

Finally, the day of the concert arrived. We weren't surprised to see a packed auditorium. I felt a tightness in my belly. I knew the audience expected to see talent. We were the talk of the town, and the money raised at our event would go to help orphans in Israel. The dancing choir went first. They danced and sang, and the audience loved it.

And then it was our turn. I propelled myself, weak legs and all, onto the stage. I took my place in the line of girls, making sure the line was straight. My heart was racing, but before I knew it the lights dimmed, the music started, and I, along with the rest of the choir, started on cue. The songs flew by more quickly than I could have thought possible, and suddenly it was time for the song in which both Rachel and I had solos. I stepped out in front and grabbed my mike, glancing over at Rachel, who was doing the same. I was shaking, but took a deep belly breath. *Think of the words, think of the meaning of the song,* came the internal reminder. Together, we began to sing...

Incredibly, after only moments, I heard a little burst, almost like a balloon popping. I wasn't sure what had happened. *Was it my voice?* No. My microphone had stopped working. *It's broken! Oh, no!* We had just reached the end of the first duet and Rachel began her part of the solo. With eyes half lidded, she held her microphone and swayed with the music. When my part came up, I took another deep breath, and pulled my microphone closer to my mouth, hoping the problem with the mike had been fixed by the techs in the sound booth. I began to sing, but could tell immediately that it was still malfunctioning. No one could hear me.

My face turned beet red, and I looked over at Rachel. She gave me a wink, and practically without missing a beat, started to sing my solo, as if that was how the song had been intended to continue. It came out so smoothly that I didn't think anyone had noticed what happened except the performers. *Wow,* I thought, *Rachel is taking over, so that I won't be embarrassed.* Part of me felt very relieved, but part of me felt sad, because I had worked so hard for this night. Lightning quick thoughts flashed through my head. *Maybe I didn't deserve this solo. I'll probably never sing again.* Then I remembered Ms. Simon's words *"Don't think of those bossy voices in your head, just think of the words of the song."* Yet, I felt really awkward standing forward on the stage doing nothing. *People are going to wonder why I'm out front but not doing any singing.* Then Rachel did an amazing thing. Still singing, she walked over to me.

I looked up and saw Rachel handing me her mike. She nodded to me, and with just a tiny hesitation, I began singing where she had left off. By then there wasn't a lot left of my part of the solo and I was about to hand the mike back to her when she put her hand over mine, keeping it in front of my mouth with a little nod. *What's she doing?* I thought. *This is her part of the solo. But, to keep things moving smoothly, she sang some of mine, so she's giving me hers. She's giving up some of her solo for me! I've got to give it my all!*

Suddenly, it seemed as if I was hearing myself sing, from outside my own body. I heard the words coming out, clear and beautiful and filling the auditorium. When I got to the part for our duet I put my arm around Rachel and tried handing back the mike. Instead, she leaned into the microphone to share it with me. Together, we sang the words of Acheinu, the audience swaying to our music. When we finished, the audience stood and clapped for us. I felt as if it had been the very best performance I could have dreamed of. Rachel had saved me from totally embarrassing myself, and our singing was real and living, not just words. As I stood there smiling, I realized how lucky I was to have such a sensitive friend, and how together we had shown the audience much more than anyone had thought possible. We had given beautiful voice to the middos of our people, to the way our people treat each other—saving one another from embarrassment.

A Chance to Shine

The Shapiro sisters are auditioning for their school play. Rochel acts and sings with ease, while Leah has to work hard at it. Leah always feels second best. What happens when both sisters try out for the lead in their school play?

Leah sat on her bedroom floor holding the script and staring into space.

"*Moshe, where are we going from here? Where do we go*?" She tried to inject emotion into her voice, like Rochel would. Leah's voice trailed off as she heard a knock on the door.

"Come in." Leah's younger sister bounced in, her auburn ponytail swinging perkily.

"How's practice going?" Rochel asked.

"I keep mixing up the lines, and I have no idea how to make it sound right," Leah said gloomily. She looked up at Rochel and sighed. Although Rochel was a year younger than Leah, she stood a head taller. *This role would be a cinch for her,* she thought, gazing at her sister. To Leah, Rochel seemed perfect. She was smart, pretty, graceful, and a quick study. Everything seemed to come so easily to her. Leah felt she was too short to look graceful, and had to work hard at most things, including memorizing. When she was acting, she often felt awkward and stilted. Yet, she still had a deep desire to get a good part in this play.

"I sound like a computer-generated voice...with a cold!" Leah groused. Rochel laughed. "Now there's a weird image!" Leah sighed. At least she knew how to make Rochel and the kids in her seventh-grade class laugh—that was something. "Wish this production was funnier," Leah said. "Maybe then I'd feel more natural with the lines."

Rochel looked over Leah's shoulder and glanced at the script. "Hmm. '*Moshe, where are we going from here? Where do we go?*'" Rochel made the lines come to life, injecting just the right amount of worry into her voice. "That's how I would say it."

Leah blinked furiously, trying to stem the flow of tears that suddenly filled her eyes. She knew Rochel would get the lead. Rochel was better at drama. *No,* Leah thought, *she's better at everything.*

"Hand me the script, and I'll help you with your lines," Rochel said. "I'll show you how I would do it."

"No, um, really, it's not necessary. I...I'll be right back," Leah stammered, snatching the script from Rochel and running out of her room.

"Where are you going, sis?" Rochel called out.

"I just need to do something," Leah yelled from the kitchen. The truth was, she needed a little space from her sister, for whom things seemed to come so easily. An idea hit her as she stood before the open fridge. Excitement filled her. *Yes, that's perfect!*

She ran to the phone and punched in a number. "Hi, Mrs. Katz. This is Leah Shapiro. I was wondering if I could make an appointment with you to read my part before tryouts next week." Leah nervously twirled a lock of sandy brown hair around a finger. "Tomorrow after school? Thank you so much!"

Mrs. Katz was the production director. She was always willing to work with anyone who needed extra practice. She had a way of helping girls improve their skills quickly, and Leah figured she was going to need all the help she could get.

With a clear plan in place, Leah ran happily back to her room. "Thanks for offering to help me practice, Rochel, but I think I've got it covered."

"Sure, no prob," Rochel answered easily. "Let me know if you change your mind. Oh, right. I came in to ask if you had a good fine-tipped black marker I could borrow? I'm making a card for Avigayil's birthday. My markers are all dried out."

Leah laughed. "Mine would be as well if I kept forgetting to put the tops back on." Leah opened her drawer and removed a pen from her neatly arranged set. "This is a really good set, so *please* put the top back on when you're done!"

"I will. It's only my own pens I forget to cover right away. Thanks!" She took the pen and, with a whirl, left the room.

The next day after school, a thin-framed Mrs. Katz appeared at Leah's locker. "Hi Leah. I thought we could work upstairs in the multipurpose room."

"Sure, okay, thanks!" Leah followed Mrs. Katz to the stairs.

When they got to the multipurpose room, Mrs. Katz started to coach Leah. "Just speak naturally, as if you were talking to a friend. Can you start from Miriam's question to Moshe?" Mrs. Katz's relaxed attitude put Leah at ease.

"*Moshe, where are we going from here? Where do we go?*" Leah spoke with ease, imitating the worry Rochel had injected into the line. Mrs. Katz's warm smile encouraged her to continue.

"*Look up, Nachshon is going....uh, look ahead?* " Leah stopped, her face turning beet red. "I'm messing it all up. I don't remember how that line goes."

"Relax, Leah, and it will come to you." Mrs. Katz put a hand lightly on Leah's shoulder. "*Look! Up ahead! Nachshon is going into the water...*"

"Look up ahead, Nachshon, he's..." Leah's trailed off. She couldn't remember the rest of the line, and even *she* could tell that her voice had no inflection. "I can't do this!" Leah stared at her feet.

"Listen, Leah," Mrs. Katz walked over and gently lifted Leah's chin, looking straight into her eyes. "You can do anything you put your mind to. You wouldn't have called me if you didn't really want to do this. It's all a question of mindset. You *will* do this, because you choose to do it."

"You really think so?"

Mrs. Katz chuckled. "I've worked with girls who were so shy that they felt like fainting when they got on stage. You just need to really focus and know that it will be great with a little extra effort." Leah smiled. They went through a few more lines and made plans to meet the following week. "Don't forget: practice, practice, practice," Mrs. Katz said, as she turned out the lights.

For the next week, as soon as Leah got home from school, she locked herself in her room and rehearsed her lines again and again, only coming out for dinner.

A week later, Leah again met with Mrs. Katz. She performed most of her part with ease. Mrs. Katz was very impressed, but something still bothered Leah.

"I know the lines, but I don't sound natural, and I can't figure out why."

"You need to say your part with sincere feeling. Put your mind into the mind of the person you are playing. Imagine how Miriam felt leaving Mitzrayim after years of slavery, how she was both thrilled and scared, ready to follow Moshe, but also uncomfortable with doing something that a slave was forbidden to do." Mrs. Katz thought a moment, then went on, "Or, think how you might feel if you were told that you were now instantly an adult, and you could go out and buy a house and start your own life. Even if you were given a guide book, wouldn't you be excited, but very unsure of yourself?"

"Oh!" Leah closed her eyes and thought about it. "Yes! I think that really helps!"

Leah finished her session with lifted spirits. She finally felt like she was making real progress. Next week was the audition, and Leah felt as ready as she ever would.

When the auditions were over, Leah saw Rochel smiling as she went to get a drink from the water fountain outside of the auditorium.

"How do you think you did?" Leah asked her sister.

"Okay, I guess." Rochel rubbed her sister's back with her warm hand. "We'll see what Hashem has in store."

And with that, Rochel walked with her bouncy gait down the hallway to greet one of her friends.

The next day, fifteen girls gathered around a piece of paper that hung on the bulletin board just outside the auditorium. Leah looked up and gasped. At the top of the sheet she saw:

MIRIAM: Rochel Shapiro

MIRIAM UNDERSTUDY and CHORUS: Leah Shapiro

Rochel had landed the lead role with only minimal practicing. Leah got second best, as the understudy. Leah knew what that meant: she would be ready to play the lead role if her sister couldn't do it. But that was not likely to happen. Rochel never missed school—ever! Leah took a deep breath and fought back her tears. She turned suddenly and ran down the hallway to bury her face in her locker, where no one could see her crying. Then, she heard a familiar voice.

"So there you are. You're disappointed, I see," said Mrs. Katz.

"I hate my life. My sister has it so easy. She is everyone's favorite, and me, well, I'm just second-rate."

Mrs. Katz gave Leah a big hug. "Hashem gives each and every one of us different abilities. Just because your sister is more natural at acting doesn't mean that you don't have a lot to offer—in fact, I would really appreciate your help creating the scenery. I know you're a talented artist. There's no one else I would trust to make it look realistic."

"But I got the UNDERSTUDY part," Leah practically sobbed. "That's like not even having a part."

"The understudy is a very important role." Mrs. Katz raised her eyebrows and continued. "You might not be performing the main role in the play this year, but the understudy to the main role is pretty close—you'll even get to lead some of the practices. Think of yourself like the vice president. If the president ever needs someone to take over running the country, the vice president does the job. Please don't give up, Leah."

Leah thought about what Mrs. Katz said, and with great determination decided that she would hang in there, just in case her sister needed her to take over. In the meantime, she would keep practicing to be the very best she could.

Rehearsals lasted for the next month and a half. Leah found that just being involved was exciting. She continued to study her part, sang in the chorus, and helped design the props and scenery as part of the stage crew. But, in private, she still wrestled with tears of disappointment.

The night before the play, Leah came home late after some last-minute work on the scenery. Her sister was lying on the couch.

"That was some dress rehearsal today, huh?" said Leah.

Rochel looked at her with glassy eyes and whispered, "I can't believe it. I'm losing my voice."

"WHAT?" Leah's mouth stayed open for a minute before Rochel replied, "I can't talk. And I feel lousy!" she croaked. Just then their mother came home from work.

"What's going on, girls?" she asked.

"Rochel's voice is all scratchy and she doesn't feel so good," Leah told her, "And our play is tomorrow!"

"Well, let's see if some hot tea and honey will help. Perhaps you've just been practicing too strenuously, Rochel, and a bit of TLC and rest will have you good as new." Rochel sipped her tea, but an hour later she was feeling even worse. Mrs. Shapiro felt

Rochel's forehead and shook her head. "Rochel, I think you are starting to run a fever. You probably aren't going to be able to perform your part, even if your voice is back tomorrow. These things usually last at least a day, if not two or three days." She looked at Leah and smiled gently, "It looks like the understudy has to step in and do her part." Leah's eyes widened in sudden realization.

"That's me! Oh! I better call Mrs. Katz and let her know!" She started to run to the phone, stopped, and ran back to the sofa. "I'm sorry Rochel, I hope you have a refuah sheleima and are all better by tomorrow morning. But, just in case, I'll let Mrs. Katz know." Rochel nodded and waved her off, letting her know she should get on with it.

"Mrs. Katz? Rochel has laryngitis and isn't feeling well. She has no voice at all and my mom thinks she's coming down with a fever," Leah told her.

"Oh no! I noticed that her voice was a bit scratchy during rehearsal today, but I thought a good night's rest would take care of it." She paused for a moment. "So, how do you feel about taking the lead tomorrow if she isn't up to it? You've done wonderfully in practice and I know you can do it. Are you ready?" Leah swallowed nervously. This is what she had wished for—to be the lead, but not for Rochel to be sick. "Leah?"

"I'm ready, Mrs. Katz. Just nervous."

"That is perfectly natural, Leah. Just take some deep breaths and tell yourself you've *got* this. You know your part and you can do it, just the way you've been doing it these last few weeks in practice."

"I will, Mrs. Katz, and thank you for all your help and encouragement!"

"You are so very welcome. I know you will shine like the star you are!"

Leah returned to Rochel. "Don't get too close to your sister," Mom cautioned as Leah began to sit on the sofa next to Rochel. "You don't want to catch whatever she has, although you might have already been exposed to it. We at least have to try to keep you from getting it." Mrs. Shapiro picked up the empty tea mug and walked out of the room. "I'll get dinner going and come back and check on you soon, Rochel."

"You must feel terrible about missing your performance," Leah sympathized as she pulled up a chair next to the sofa. "I know I would. I'm sorry I'm taking your place."

"S'okay," Rochel rasped. "The show must go on. I know you'll do a great job tomorrow! You've gotten really good these past few weeks!"

"But I'm really nervous. I thought I wanted the lead role. I wanted to be able to act just like you. You always have such confidence and seem so natural." She took a deep breath and continued, "But now that I have the role, I'm not so sure I really want it."

Rochel was quiet a moment, toying with the tassels on the throw her mother had placed over her. "Want to know a secret?" she rasped.

"What?" Leah wondered.

"First of all, you're really great at so many things." Rochel looked at her sister. "You are a super artist. All the scenery you did is wonderful. And second, last year when I had my first lead, I was horribly nervous—my knees kept knocking together." Rochel smiled. "I was so hard on myself."

"What do you mean?" Leah leaned closer to hear better. Rochel held up a hand in warning, "Germs! Back off!" Leah smiled and moved back a bit.

"Well, I might have been doing great job. At least, everyone said so, but in my mind, I was about to ruin the show." Rochel took a deep breath. "I kept thinking I was too loud, or too fake sounding, or not loud enough. And whenever I thought those things, I made more mistakes than ever. So, after I almost lost the part because I kept messing up, Mrs. Katz told me to stop thinking so much, just picture myself as the part I was playing, and let it happen."

"Yeah, she told me it was all about my mindset," Leah agreed.

"I learned that if I don't relax and trust that my practicing is enough—and stop criticizing myself, I make more mistakes. Mrs. Katz said that it undermines the foundation we build, like building a beautiful building on quicksand. We have to have firm ground under us *before* we start putting up the building. In this case, I think it's the confidence that if we do our very best, that is all we can do."

Leah thought about that. "So, I guess once I've learned the part and done all I can to be the character I'm playing, I should just…what? Assume I'm going to do it well?"

"Yep. A good attitude can boost a person's talent to the next level." Rochel let out a raspy laugh. "Do me…no, scratch that. Do *us* proud!"

Leah smiled. "I will. I might still have butterflies, but I know the part. I can do this."

And, she did. For the next three days, Leah went on stage and gave it her all. Yes, her legs were all a-tremble that first show, and sure, she missed a line here or there. But with each performance, her confidence grew. One night both she and her co-actress muffed their lines, and Leah improvised by cracking a joke, causing the audience to roar with laughter. After each performance, friends and parents let her know how well they thought she had played the part.

Rochel came to every show, throat lozenges in mouth and balloons in hand for her sister. The first night's balloons read: "Congratulations, *you're a star*!" The second night they announced: *"You did great!"* And for the finale, Rochel found a huge balloon that read: "Super Star!"

Taking her final bow, Leah couldn't believe it was over. She felt high as a kite. Mrs. Katz gave her an extra thank you for rising to the occasion and told Leah that she enjoyed her creative humor. She handed Leah a small wrapped gift for helping to create the stunning props and scenery, as well as being in the choir.

Rochel came over and gave her a big hug, with a huge, carefree smile.

"I'm sorry I took your place, Rochel," Leah said. "I feel like it should be you getting all this attention and praise. And..."

"No, don't say another word!" Rochel interrupted. "Hashem meant it to be this way. I knew you could do it and that you would be fantastic if you could just get rid of your self-doubt. And you did! You were wonderful!"

"But aren't you even the least bit sorry it happened? Aren't you...well, a bit annoyed, upset, even jealous that it was me that played the main part instead of you?"

"Well, I am sorry that I didn't get to be a part of the show. That's always so exciting, being with everyone right before and after a show. But no, I don't feel bad that you had the part instead of me. I *liked* seeing you up there. And, truth be told, I'm glad not to have had to deal with the jitters before each show. Getting sick drained all my energy. I was happy to just be an observer. So, stop fretting and enjoy this moment. You ARE a star!"

And for the first time, Leah realized that she had absolutely nothing to be jealous of. She had talents all her own, and her sister was truly there for her. She could love Rochel right back without the least twinge of self-doubt.

Fun & Facts

Halbanas Panim - הלבנת פנים

Embarrassment – Whitening of the face.

Some things seem harmless on the surface, but in truth can be truly embarrassing and seriously damaging.

A Blush: Is it Cute or Embarrassing?

What do *you* think? Sometimes, when we are fairly young, people think that our blushing is "cute." "Aw, she's blushing," someone will say. "Isn't that adorable?" But most often the one blushing does not think so.

Why? When something happens in our body that others can see (or hear) and that we have no control over, we feel embarrassment. What other things can you think of that fall into this category?

How can we make someone feel more comfortable when they blush, right from the beginning?

Did You know? When people feel shame or are nervous or embarrassed, their nervous system releases a chemical, a stress hormone called adrenaline. The adrenaline dilates the blood vessels of the face, neck and sometimes chest, causing more blood to flow through them. Because these tiny veins are closer to the surface of the skin, the extra blood flow makes the face and neck look red. This is what we call blushing. The amazing thing is, this usually *only* happens to the face neck and sometimes the chest, but not the rest of the body. For most people, turning red or feeling hot in the face doesn't last long.

Some people feel embarrassment in a way that is more like shock or fright. In such cases a person often gets white in the face, rather than red. This is where the Hebrew term *halbanos panim*—whitening of the face—comes from. This happens when the chemicals epinephrine and norepineprine in your body cause the blood vessels in your skin to contract. With less blood flowing in your face, it appears much paler, or white.

Think:

Why did Hashem make it possible for us to see when someone is embarrassed? Does blushing or seeing someone blush make us more sensitive to how our actions or speech affects others?

The Positive:

Blushing can be good if we feel bad about what we did and it stops us from doing something wrong again. Scientists studying blushing have learned that "people are more likely to forgive and view favorably someone who has committed an embarrassing act, if he or she is visibly blushing." When people see someone blush, they feel that the person truly is sorry for whatever they have said or done and believe they will not do so again.

Crozier, R. "The Puzzel of Blushing," *The Psychologist*, 05/2010, Volume 23, Issue 5, (May 2010)

Cool Fact:

Children don't blush until they are two or three years old. That is because children first have to know what is right and wrong, or proper and improper, in order to feel embarrassment or shame.

(Gwyneth Doherty-Sneddon. *Children's Unspoken Languages,* London, NY: Jessica Kingsley Publishers Ltd, 2003.)

Interesting Fact:

For some people blushing is even more embarrassing, because once they blush, their face stays red for hours. You can imagine how difficult this might be for them. It can even cause people to lose their jobs. In one instance, a saleswoman couldn't do her job because people didn't feel comfortable with her constant blushing. She was almost fired, but then discovered there was a kind of surgery that could help her.

Interview: A Doctor's Tale

Dr. David Nielson, from San Antonio, Texas, performs a special surgery to help people with this prolonged blushing problem.

Surgery to control blushing? Let's find out more as we talk with Dr. Nielson, a doctor in San Antonio, Texas

Hi Dr. Nielson, can you tell us what happens to a person with a bad blushing problem?

In these cases, when someone is scared, nervous, ashamed, or embarrassed, the brain sends out way too strong a signal. It releases chemicals that bombard the body, which results in a feeling of too much heat in the face and neck, and a deep red color that lasts for hours, even after the nervous feeling has passed.

Can you imagine what these people have to go through? Walking around red in the face and feeling extreme heat for hours. That in itself is embarrassing and can cause a person to lose their focus on whatever they are doing. In fact, over time, the blushing or burning causes a person to become too focused on anything that might start it. These people are constantly nervous because they never know when their face will suddenly heat up and turn bright red. They lose their self-confidence and usually don't like getting together with friends or mingling in crowds, wishing to avoid people and stay safely alone, at home.

How do you help these cases?

I meet with patients to see if surgery is a good choice for them. Usually every other possible method, like certain medicines or feedback therapy, is used first. If those methods don't work, surgery becomes an option. If we decide that it is a good choice, I perform a surgery called Microscopic ETS (endoscopic thoracic sympathectomy). That is, I basically make a small incision and cut the nerves in the upper spine that signal the body to blush.

Are there any side effects of the surgery?

Yes. Interestingly enough, the most common side-effect is that people sweat on their backs and center chests, and sometimes on their legs or feet. While that may be unpleasant, for most people that is easier to handle than something that is visible on one's face where everyone can see it.

Do you have any success stories?

Yes. I performed surgery recently on a man who had uncontrollable blushing. It was so bad that he honestly felt hopeless. He had trouble at work and at home. Other easier types of treatments didn't help him, so we decided that surgery was for him. Following his surgery he was amazed at the instant results. He told us that he feels like a new person. For example, he is now able to talk in public without blushing. His nervousness is gone. Years of suffering and worry were improved in one instant. He told me that he can now function at work and in his personal life without worry of sweating (on his forehead), blushing, or being embarrassed.

Wow! Thank you, Dr. Nielson for all of your great work, best of luck.

****

The Science:
There are nerves in the body called **sympathetic nerves** that are part of the autonomic nervous system. The autonomic nervous system is responsible for controlling those bodily functions that are not conscious, like our breathing, and our heartbeat. The sympathetic nerves control the way our blood vessels constrict and dilate.

The surgery for cutting the nerves that control our facial blushing and sweating can be done either in the upper spine or under the armpits. This will usually stop excessive sweating on the face, blushing and hand sweating. However, some patients report that the benefits have not lasted or that the side effect of sweating on other parts of the body is not worth it. Deciding to do the surgery should be based upon having tried every other method to reduce the blushing and upon how severe the blushing is and how badly it interferes with one's everyday life. Some people have reported that their blushing diminishes as they get older and become surer of themselves in various situations. Confidence and being relaxed can help a great deal.

For Klal Yisroel, trusting that everything comes from Hashem and striving to just do our best helps many people stay calm and reduce the stresses that contribute to excessive blushing.

(Personal Communication, Dr. David H. Nielson, Hyperhidrosis USA, January 5, 2015.)

Think!

It's an aveira to embarrass or shame another person. The Torah goes so far as to say that shaming a person is the same as killing him or spilling blood. Can you guess why? Have you ever experienced the deep pain of being embarrassed by another in a public setting? Not only does this affect you, but also the way others think of you. Not only are you embarrassed at that moment, but the shame makes you want to avoid all those who witnessed your embarrassment forever after.

True Story: The Smell of Garlic

Rabbi Yehudah ha-Nasi couldn't stand the smell of garlic. In fact, if one of his talmidim (students) smelled of garlic, Rabbi Yehudah ha-Nasi was unable to teach. All of his talmidim knew this, and were very careful never to eat garlic before attending his classes. One day, though, as the Rav began to teach, he smelled a strong odor of garlic. "Whoever had garlic, please leave so that I may continue teaching," he requested. At that, one of the Rav's top students, Rav Chiyya, stood up and walked out of the room so as not to embarrass the talmid who ate the garlic. Knowing that he was not the culprit, the rest of the class got up and walked out so as not to embarrass Rav Chiyya. The next day, Rav Yehudah ha-Nasi's son asked Rav Chiyya if indeed he was the student who ate the garlic. Rav Chiyya explained to him that he knew another student ate it, but he didn't want that student to be embarrassed.

(Talmud, *Sanhedrin* 11a)

What a great act of chesed (kindness) it is to extend ourselves and save another from embarrassment!

Chapter Four

Who Is This, Really?

Ayin Tovah – עין טובה

Seeing With an Eye

That Looks for the Good

Mystery of the Close Call

Shira really gets on the nerves of her classmates. She doesn't do it on purpose—but kids make fun of her anyway.

I used to sit next to Shira in Chumash class. Often, during the time our teacher, Mrs. Klein, gave out homework assignments, Shira would pepper me with seemingly pointless questions. "What did you and Yehudis do last Sunday?" "Was it fun?" "Would you wear a red skirt?" "Did you know that your backpack actually has a zipper with a pocket under the yellow seam?" (I didn't.) "Where did you buy your new shoes?" Why was she so nosy? Mostly, I would just shush her or try to ignore her. Sometimes Mrs. Klein would blame me for talking during class, and I would get into trouble even though it wasn't my fault. Other times it was Shira who would end up getting into trouble. Either way, the whole situation was uncomfortable.

Another thing that bothered me about Shira was her chair. Somehow, it always ended up sliding right into mine. Once, she stood up so fast at the end of class that her chair crashed into me, knocking me to the floor. The entire class turned to stare, some outright laughing. So humiliating!

Shira's papers were always falling on the floor or creeping onto my desk; her math papers mixed up with her Ivrit notes and her new spelling lists piled haphazardly upon old spelling tests. Being near Shira made me feel as if her manner and mess would spill over onto *me*, causing people to think that I was like her. I wanted to be far away from her.

Why does Shira act like this? And why is she so disorganized and klutzy? I wondered. *Why can't she just be normal?* It seemed to me that she acted this way on purpose. After all, she never apologized or acted embarrassed by any of her behavior.

Then, one day during lunch period, it seemed that all the teachers were abuzz with some hidden news. They stood talking in the hallways in small groups, but stopped as soon as a student got close. Rabbi Stein, our principal, walked with particular determination through the school, a look of deep concern on his face. His usual friendly greeting to those he passed was absent. What was going on? All of us wondered.

"Know what happened?" I turned, and there was Shira, standing a little too close.

"Huh?" I stammered.

"The teachers, know what they're all talking about?"

"No, we were wondering why they all seem to be so distracted and worried," I said.

Shira shifted her backpack to her other shoulder and smiled. "All the new computers are missing," she informed me conspiratorially.

"What computers?" I hadn't heard anything about new computers.

"The school ordered a whole batch of the latest laptops for the computer room for our computer courses. They were delivered yesterday, but now they're all missing," Shira explained.

"What! Really? How do you know?" I asked her.

"I asked Mrs. Klein. She told me." Mrs. Klein worked in the office. I looked at Shira with wonder. No one else would have had the temerity, the total lack of self-consciousness to just go and ask in the office.

"Do they have any idea where the computers are?" I asked her.

"Not a clue," she shook her head. "Wanna help me figure it out, Aviva?" I hesitated.

"How do you expect to figure it out if the whole administration can't?" I asked her.

"It's a mystery. I love solving mysteries. We can follow the clues and see where they lead. So, want to help?" She looked at me brightly, waiting for my answer.

"I guess." I wanted to know what happened, but wasn't sure looking for clues with Shira was either smart or helpful. Spend time with someone like Shira? Did I want that? But, then, no one else I knew would take it upon herself to try and figure this out. Truthfully, I was fascinated by the possibility.

"Where do we start?" I had no idea myself. Shira tapped a finger to her chin.

"Well, first we need to find out where exactly the computers were delivered and see if any clues are there." That seemed reasonable, so we went to the office to see if they would tell us where the computers had been brought in. Shira just went right in and asked, and Mrs. Klein was willing to answer.

"Oh, all the boxes were brought in through the lunchroom delivery entrance," she told us.

"And then what?" asked Shira. "What was supposed to happen to the boxes?"

"Well," Mrs. Klein thought a bit, "I suppose they were to be put away until it was time to use them.

"*Where* were they supposed to be put?" Shira persisted. "And who was supposed to do the putting?"

"I don't really know the answers," Mrs. Klein said, "you'll have to ask the computer teacher. She probably knows. Now, I've got to get back to work, if you ladies will excuse me?" and with that she turned to go into the inner office.

"Thanks Mrs. Klein!" we both called to her retreating back.

"Next step, Mrs. Mandel?" I asked Shira. I was getting into the groove of this quest for answers. Mrs. Mandel was our Computers teacher. She taught programming, Microsoft Office and some graphics programs like Photoshop.

"You've got it!" Shira smiled happily, "on to the next phase of our investigation. I glanced at the time. There were only fifteen minutes left until the bell.

"We'll have to make this quick, lunch is almost over," I warned.

"That's okay," Shira said easily, "we can continue during fifth period. Mrs. Lerman is out today so we'll have a study period." I stared at her.

"How in the world do you know that?" Usually no one knew when a teacher was absent until they didn't show up for class and we had a substitute.

"I saw her leaving the building and asked her where she was going. She told me she had to take her daughter to the doctor and she wouldn't be back for class."

"Oh." I was still a bit awed by how much Shira seemed to find out about things. I was beginning to see her in a different light. She might ask a lot of questions, but maybe it wasn't a bad thing. Annoying sometimes, sure. But, maybe not so pointless. We climbed to the third floor and found Mrs. Mandel adjusting cables in the computer room.

"Hi, Mrs. Mandel," Shira smiled as we walked over.

"Shira, Aviva, what brings you here?"

"We were wondering. If the computers were delivered to the lunchroom, were they supposed to be brought here?"

Mrs. Mandel seemed a bit taken aback that Shira knew so much about what was happening. I could see her trying to decide whether to answer us or not. Then she shrugged.

"I guess it can't hurt to tell you if you already know so much," she sighed. "I'm not ready to set them up here yet. We need to move some of these old computers out first. The boxes of new computers were supposed to be put in the beis medrash and stacked on the shelves there, but they never showed up. I don't know how I'm supposed to teach the next semester's curriculum without them." She shook her head. "Such an expensive loss, too!"

The beis medrash in our school wasn't quite like one that could be found in the boys' yeshivos, a place where they studied Gemara. For us it was a room where girls could go to study quietly during lunch and for Rabbi Stein to gather a few classes and give a lesson in mussar (character development). A few of the rebbeim, as well as Rabbi Stein, often went there to learn in between classes as well.

If the boxes never showed up, I thought, then the next question was...

"Well, who was supposed to put the boxes in the beis medrash?" I asked.

"And when was it supposed to happen?" added Shira. She was leaning on the desk and somehow knocked over a vase with silk flowers.

"Good questions, but I don't know the answers," Mrs. Mandel told us. "I guess you'll have to ask Rabbi Stein." Shira quickly set the vase upright and put the silk flowers back in, not quite as neatly as they had been before.

"Okay, thanks Mrs. Mandel!" she sang out, just as the bell rang. Shira and I went to class. Throughout the next period I was filled with excitement, waiting to continue our investigation. I didn't know if we would solve the mystery, but it was fun trying. Sure enough, when fifth period started, a substitute came in and told us we had a free period. I asked to be excused and waited for Shira outside the room. Shira came out a few minutes later.

"Do you think Rabbi Stein will really answer our questions?" I worried. "I mean, why would he want us involved anyway. I'm sure he's looking into this himself."

"Don't worry so much," Shira answered, "people who are troubled *like* when others are trying to help." Shira started off toward the principal's office. *How did she have so much confidence?* I wondered as I quickly caught up. *Or did she just not realize that someone like Rabbi Stein might not like students butting into his business?* I was a little bit put off and a little amazed at Shira's sheer force of will, because I usually didn't like bothering people. Shira seemed not to notice if she bothered anyone. Or, maybe, she didn't see what she did as bothersome. We got to the office just as Rabbi Stein was walking out.

"Excuse me, Rabbi Stein," Shira spoke. Rabbi Stein stopped and looked at us inquiringly. "We're trying to help solve this case of the missing computers," Shira informed him, "and need a few of the important details."

"Miss Caplan, I don't think..." Rabbi Stein began.

"No, no, don't worry," Shira cut in, "we won't get in your way. Would it be possible for you to just answer two questions?"

"We're sorry to bother you, Rabbi Stein," I added quickly, "but Shira and I really think we might be able to help. At least, we're trying to." Rabbi Stein hesitated a moment, then nodded.

Shira sighed happily and asked, "Who was supposed to move the boxes of computers and when was it supposed to happen?" Rabbi Stein started to shake his head, but Shira kept right on going.

"We're not trying to blame anyone. I'm sure you already made sure that whoever it was didn't take them, chas v'shalom, but it would help us follow the clues if we could just know who it was so we can rule out any other possibilities, you know? Please? We just want to help and we won't get in your way and we won't spread lashon hora about anyone, right?" Shira finished in a rush, looking at me. I nodded in agreement.

Rabbi Stein considered us a moment. I was really worried that he would be offended at Shira's manner. It seemed too forward, not kavodik (respectful) enough. But Rabbi Stein looked at Shira and then said, "I'll answer your questions, but I'm trusting you to be careful with the information. Do you understand? No accusing anyone and you come to me directly if you think of anything that might be helpful. Don't speak about it with other students. Can I trust you both with this?"

We nodded solemnly. This was serious. And I realized that Rabbi Stein was wise to see that Shira didn't mean anything bad in her attitude. That it was just her way.

"The janitor brought the boxes in with the delivery men yesterday evening." Rabbi Stein told us. "He was supposed to bring them to the beis medrash this morning, but when he came in, the boxes were missing. As you may have already heard, it doesn't seem the building was broken into overnight and there is no one we don't trust who works in this building. It really is a mystery what happened to those boxes. Do your investigating," he said with a faint smile, "perhaps Hashem will give you success where we have failed so far." He walked off and we stood thinking.

"What next?" I asked Shira, "Any ideas?"

"Well, we could talk to the janitor, but I don't know how that will help. It looks like he doesn't know what happened. But, we should ask just in case."

"Those had to be a lot of boxes. I bet they were too heavy to move without some sort of help. I wonder how he was planning on moving them," I pondered.

"Excellent reasoning, Watson!" Shira approved.

"Who's Watson?" I asked.

"Oh, he was Sherlock Holmes's friend who helped him solve crimes and mysteries. Sherlock Holmes was a famous detective in fiction stories. I've read all of them."

"Uh, okay, so, I'm Watson and you're Sherlock Holmes?"

"In the book, Watson was always coming up with ideas and Sherlock would say things like, 'excellent deduction, Watson,' so when you had a good idea, that's what I said."

I blinked and shook my head. "All right, so let's go ask the janitor some questions...Sherlock."

"Right you are, Watson," Shira quipped back.

We searched the school until we found the janitor on the second floor, cleaning up in the science lab.

"Hi Juan!" we chorused. "Can we ask you a few questions?

"Questions?" he looked confused.

"We just want to know what exactly happened when the computers came," Shira told him.

"I already tell Rabbi Stein," he said, "he know I not take them. I'm honest man," he sounded worried.

"Don't worry, Juan, we know it wasn't you. But we want to help find out where they are. Don't you think it would be neat if you helped us figure it all out?"

"I not know where they are. I help unload them. I do my other jobs. I come back in morning. They gone," Juan sighed. He began lining up clean beakers on a tray.

"Well, how were you going to move them to the beis medrash? You weren't going to carry every box there, right?" I asked.

"Not carry. Use cart from kitchen. I tell Anita to bring cart when we ready to move boxes. But not needed because boxes not there." Juan looked at us and held his hands open to either side. "They all just...gone."

"When did you come back and find them gone?" Shira asked next.

"What, when?" Juan was confused.

"I mean, what time was it? Was it in the evening still or in the morning?"

"All the boxes, they there in the evening when I go home. In the morning I come in at six and they all there. I go first to clean the bathrooms. When I finish, no boxes."

"Who else was here when you came?" I asked.

"Nobody here. I first one." I ran out of questions.

"So who was the first one to come in after you?" Shira persisted.

Juan stood and thought a bit, rubbing his chin. "Anita and kitchen staff come in at seven. I not see who come in first." Juan shrugged and sighed, "I need to finish. Lot of work here."

"Okay, Juan, thanks!" I smiled.

"Ehh...," he stopped our leaving.

"Yes?" Shira asked.

"You find boxes, you tell me, yes?" he pleaded.

"Absolutely! Yes!" we assured him.

As we walked down the hall, we thought about all that we had been told. *Where could those boxes be? Who had taken them?*

"Did you buy those socks at Target?" Shira asked out of nowhere. I looked down at my argyle blue and yellow socks.

"Uh, I think so," I responded. Usually, when she asked a question that seemed nosy, I didn't want to answer. Now, suddenly, I wanted to know why she asked such annoying questions. “Why do you want to know?”

“I went to Suzie’s with my mother to buy socks, but I didn’t get any because I like blue and yellow like you’re wearing and they didn’t have anything in those colors.”

Oh. I guess she had a reason that made sense. I was getting a feel for her questions. They were kind of whatever popped into her head at that moment, but had some reason behind them. Sometimes they were out of place with what was happening, but nothing was really wrong or bad about her questions. They were just a little…well, odd? Out of context?

“I’ll ask my Mom. She bought them for me,” I told her. Then we were back to trying to decide where to go in our investigation when the bell rang for the next period.

“Meet me in the lunchroom after school!” Shira called as she ran off.

“You have an idea?” I called back.

“Maybe. Just, be there!” she insisted and disappeared around the corner.

That afternoon we had a “Middah of the Month” shmuz. That’s when a few classes are crowded into one room and several morahs (teachers) speak on a particular topic, often teaching us songs and techniques to help us really “get” a concept. Shira’s class came in and everyone found places to sit. Today’s topic was ve’ahavta lereiacha kamocha…you should love your fellow like yourself. It wasn’t a new idea. We all grew up with these words. But these sessions helped us really bring the ideas alive in our day-to-day living. Well, not always. Sometimes it was hard to think about these ideas. Today it was especially difficult. All I could think about was solving the mystery.

Today's assignment was to think about our partners and think of their unique qualities. We were told to fill a page with as many good qualities as we could about our assigned partner. Shira scooted in beside me and said, "I'll be your partner, okay?" I couldn't say no, not with her looking expectantly at me with her big, happy brown eyes. We each were told to fill a page with as many genuine compliments about our partner as we could and bring them back the next day. As I walked from class, two of my friends accompanied me to the next room for History.

"Sorry you got saddled with Shira," said Yehudis, "She slipped in too fast for me to be partners with you."

"Yeah," chimed in Rina, "what can you even write about her? Let's see; weird, nosy, loud..."

"Clumsy, awkward, big eyed," Yehudis added with a giggle.

"Good at knocking over chairs..." both girls broke into laughter, and for a moment I joined them. It felt good to be laughing with my friends, but at the same time I felt a little guilty. After all, Shira and I were on an adventure. You don't speak about your adventure partner like that. I didn't even quite see her like that any longer. She was actually a lot of fun, in her odd way. And I was getting used to her manner so that I barely noticed it.

"What are you going to write about Nava," I asked Yehudis about her partner, changing the focus.

"Oh, that's easy," Yehudis smiled, "Nava is the best artist in the whole school, so I can say she is artistic, creative, neat, organized, friendly and fun to play Chinese jump rope with at recess!"

"And I'm gonna write that Simma is funny, pretty and always saves me a place on line!" Rina told us. "I'll think of something else to add 'cause even though she sometimes seems snobby, she really is a good person and that's what counts!"

Hearing them speak about their partners made me feel even worse about our laughing about Shira. This was supposed to be about ahavas Yisroel, about *loving our fellow Jew like oneself*—not about finding faults. The truth was, I really *could* think of good things to write about Shira. She was friendly, interesting, adventurous, observant and bold. She was a lot of fun to be around and after spending time with her, amazingly, I *was* getting to like her—a whole lot. While it was fun laughing with the other girls and being part of the group, I realized that laughing about others was not the kind of laughing we should be doing.

"I think Shira has some really good qualities!" I blurted. "I'm going to write about those."

Rina and Yehudis paused in the middle of their conversation and looked at me.

"Ve'ahavta," I said. "Right?" They both looked a bit guilty, then nodded. Our History teacher began the lesson and our conversation ended.

When school let out, I made my way to the lunchroom. Shira was already there, impatiently shifting from foot to foot.

"Hi Shira! I don't know if I can stay and do more investigating right now because my carpool will be leaving in five minutes."

"Oh, don't worry, my Mom will drive you home. I already called her and she agreed."

"Really? Super! I'll just run out and tell the other girls to let the carpool driver know not to wait for me."

"Okay, I'll be here." Shira said as I ran out to do just that.

When I got back I saw that Shira was speaking with one of the ladies who work in the lunchroom. I joined her and heard her say, "So, you saw all the boxes when you came in at seven, but didn't see them an hour later?"

"That's right," the woman answered. "I passed them and went into the kitchen and started prepping for breakfast."

"Who else was here besides you, Anita?" Shira asked.

"Well, I saw Juan going about his business, and then there was Isabel and Emma, my helpers. There is also Alma, but she is new and just training. I'm trying to teach her to begin taking initiative and start helping where it is needed instead of always waiting to be told what to do, but it takes time, you know?" Shira nodded, as if she understood. Personally, I wasn't sure what she was talking about.

"That's it? Just the three of you and the new helper?"

"Yes, we do all the breakfast work. I already asked Isabel and Emma and they said they saw the boxes when they came in and they were gone when they next left the kitchen."

"Okay, thanks Anita!" Shira said. "Do you mind if we look around a bit? For clues?"

"No, that's fine," she nodded, "we stay half an hour more." She turned to go back into the kitchen. Shira looked around and called, "Wait! Which carts were you going to use to move the computers?" Anita looked around and pointed to serving carts with three levels lined up against the back wall.

"Those are the ones, but now we don't need them so I'll have Juan bring them back into the kitchen." Anita went into the kitchen and Shira grabbed my sleeve.

"Come on!" she said. "We need to check out those carts before they get moved."

"Uh, why?" I asked as I was ushered to the back of the room. "What good will it do us if they were never used?"

"That's what we need to find out! If they were moved, someone *had* to have used the carts. It only makes sense. How else would they have gotten all those boxes moved so quickly?"

"Right," I agreed. We stopped at the carts and looked them over. I wasn't sure what evidence I could find on a metal cart, but after examining two of them I saw something caught in the wheel of the third.

"Look here, Shira! There's something caught here." I started tugging at the piece of ... what was this brown thing? "It's a torn piece of cardboard!" I told her excitedly. "Help me get it free. Push the cart so the wheels will move and I'll pull on the piece."

"Yes!" Shira exclaimed, "Our first real break in the case!" She took hold of the cart and slowly rolled it away from me as I pulled on the piece. It pulled out slowly and then with a last snap I held the piece in my hand. Shira rushed over to examine it with me.

"Look at the letters!" Shira pointed. "It's a crooked 'e' and two 'l's and below is a bit of a letter followed by 'any'."

"I know the look of these letters, I think," I told her. "It looks like the way 'Dell' is written on my computer at home."

"And, and ... just maybe, that at the bottom is the end of the word, Company?" We looked at each other, excitement and wonder in our eyes. Suddenly I had a thought and looked around quickly, spotting just what I was looking for.

"The garbage!" I said, "if a box got stuck and torn, maybe someone threw the rest of it in the garbage!" We looked at the full bin sitting by the carts, then realized there were four or five other bins sitting around the room, all full to the brim with the day's refuse.

"Uh, I'm not going through all those garbage cans just on the possibility that there *might* be a torn up box in one. There's no way to know which bin it could be in," I said, feeling frustrated.

Shira looked down at her shoes, at the cart, at the wheel that had trapped the piece of cardboard, her lip caught thoughtfully between her teeth. Then her eyes opened wide.

"Look Aviva! This cart left a faint black trail when we moved it!" She was right. I could see a faint black streak from where I stood to where the cart had been moved. I looked around the floor and saw more streaks of faint black.

"The cart's been moved all over this floor, Shira. We won't be able to tell where it was or where it ended up."

"Not *in* the dining room," Shira said slowly, "but…" she grinned widely, "if it was wheeled anywhere *outside* the dining room…"

"We can follow it!" we both said at once. "Ok, you check the main hall entrance," Shira instructed. "I'll check the back way to the auditorium." With a nod, I ran to see if there were any tracks on the tiles outside the door of the dining room in the main hall. I looked, but saw nothing. Running back into the room, I saw Shira running back in as well. She shook her head and pointed to the side entrance that led to the storage rooms.

I nodded and ran to look there, while Shira ran off to the far wall. When I came back, I didn't see her anywhere in the room. There were no other entrances to the lunchroom except for the kitchen. Was she in there? I took a step and suddenly Shira was there.

"Where...?" I began but was interrupted by an excited Shira.

"There's an *elevator* behind this door!" She exclaimed. "I always thought it was a storage cabinet. But it's an elevator and it goes down to the lower level."

"What's down there?" I wondered. It certainly wasn't classrooms.

"I think it's the water heaters and heating and air conditioning and pipes and stuff. But the best news is, there's a faint black trail inside the elevator. Come on! This has got to be it!"

I ran over to the door and sure enough, there was an elevator door behind it. We pushed the button, the door slid open and in we went. Shira pushed the LL button. When the door opened, I saw a long passageway with pillars on the left with a large space behind them and some doors on the right. We stepped out and followed the faint black line left by the wheel of the cart and saw that it turned toward a closed door. Taking a deep breath, I tried the handle. The door was locked.

"There's a window in the door, but it's too high for either of us to see through." Shira looked around for something to climb on, but there was nothing. "Boost me up?" she asked. I clasped my hands together and leaned down. Shira placed a foot on my makeshift step and I stood up to boost her higher, looking up to see if it was high enough. I wasn't strong enough to hold the position for more than a few seconds and warned, "I'm losing it! Letting you down!" I lowered her quickly and practically fell over, but Shira grabbed me and steadied me.

"We found them!" she exclaimed triumphantly. "All the computers are set up on desks in that room!"

"Really?" I was amazed. "What in the world are they doing down here? And set up on desks? Is this a secret teaching room or something?" We stared at each other, both trying to fathom what this could mean.

Finally, Shira shrugged. "I don't know why they're here or how they got here, but at least we found them." I nodded and looked around.

"It's kind of creepy down here," I told her. "It's even weirder to find all the computers set up all the way down in this part of the school where no students are supposed to go."

Shira scrunched up her face and said in a put-on accent, "Eez a secret training room for zee spies. Eef zey catch us, zey vill put us in a room and vill trow avay za key."

I burst out laughing and shook my head. "Okay, thanks for bringing some silly into this. But I sure would like to know the what and why of this."

"Let's go talk to Anita and her helpers again," Shira advised. "I have a few more questions."

We started to troop back to the elevator, but Shira stopped suddenly and asked, "Do you have a Dell computer at home?" Was this another of Shira's awkward questions?

"I do. My father bought a new one for his work and I get to use it for homework sometimes. Why did you ask?"

"Look!" She pointed off to the left, where there were no lights on and the pillars cast shadows from the lights on our side of the passageway. I followed her gaze and saw two piles of boxes that had been broken down and piled neatly. The top one had large bold letters that read: **Dell Inspiron 13 5000.**

"In case we had any doubts, here's the proof," Shira said.

"We've solved the case!" I enthused. "That is one of the latest computers so those boxes couldn't have been there a long time."

"Well, it's almost solved," Shira said, "we have the computers, which, I guess, is the most important part, but how they got here is still a mystery."

"Okay, onward Sherlock," I joked. We ran back to the elevator and went up and into the kitchen, where Anita was giving last minute instructions to her helpers.

"Hi Anita!" we chorused.

"You still here?" she asked, "I thought you left with all the other girls. What are you still doing here?"

"We'll be leaving in a minute," Shira said, "but, we just wanted to double check our facts. You said you asked all your helpers if they had anything to do with those boxes, right?"

Anita nodded her head, "Yes, they came straight into the kitchen and both of them saw the boxes. When we came out to set up the tables, the boxes were gone."

"What time was it when they saw the computers, do you remember?" I asked.

"It was probably about 7:10, because we had to be ready for breakfast. They were running a bit late," Anita admitted.

"And absolutely no one else was here?" I wanted to be sure.

"No one. Well, except for the new girl, Alma. She came into the kitchen right about eight all out of breath and trying to tell me how helpful she was, but I wasn't having any of her excuses.

She needed to be here with us at seven sharp." Anita's lips firmed, remembering the incident.

I had a sudden thought. I looked at Shira and saw her mouth open, eyes brimming with excitement. She had the same idea.

"May we speak with Alma for just a few seconds, please?" I asked Anita.

"Well, you could, but she called in sick today. You'll have to wait until tomorrow when she comes back," she told us.

"But this can't wait!" Shira cried. "Can we call her?"

"You'd have to get Rabbi Stein's permission for that. I can't give out her phone number."

"Okay, thanks Anita!" we said and raced off to find Rabbi Stein, who was usually in his office for an hour or so after the school closed.

"Hope he's still here!" Shira panted.

"Well, if he's trying to deal with the computer problem, he probably is," I suggested.

We ran to his office and saw that the door was closed. Not a good sign, but hopefully, he was still in there. I knocked. And waited. Shira bounced with impatience, but we knocked once more and waited.

"I guess he left," I said. "It will have to wait until tomorrow morning." I was really disappointed, but knew that nothing would really change in that time.

"Yeah," Shira sighed gloomily. "I'll call my mom and tell her we're ready to be picked up." We started walking to the front of the school where there was a payphone for the girls to use. When we got there, we were surprised to see Rabbi Stein standing outside the glass doors speaking with a policeman.

There was a police car parked outside the building. Shira and I exchanged a quick look of understanding and rushed outside.

"Excuse us Rabbi Stein," I said, a bit breathlessly.

"Not right now, girls," he said gently, "I'm in the middle of things here and it would be best if you went back inside if you are waiting for your ride."

"But, Rabbi Stein, we found them!" Shira burst out.

"What?" he looked surprised. "You found the computers?"

"Yes!" I added, "They're in a room down in the basement. All set up on old desks!"

The policeman raised his eyebrows at this and asked, "Do you still wish to file that report? We can investigate to find out what happened and who was responsible, if you wish," he added.

"One moment, please," Rabbi Stein told him and turned back to us. "Are you sure these are the laptops we're looking for?" he asked us.

"We didn't go into the room," Shira said, "but they look like new laptops and we saw piles of boxes that were taken apart that had DELL printed on them."

Rabbi Stein lifted his eyes and called out, "Baruch Hashem!" He looked back at us. "You girls have lifted a very heavy burden from my shoulders," he said, "please just wait a moment while I finish with this police officer."

He spoke with the policeman a few more minutes, shook his hand, and the officer got back in his car and drove off.

"Now," Rabbi Stein turned to us, "can you show me where the computers are? We can call whomever is coming to pick you up and have them delay a bit, hmmm?"

"Sure, Rabbi Stein!" Shira answered eagerly, "I don't think my mother will mind as long as we call her right away." We all went into Rabbi Stein's office where Shira immediately called her mother. Her mother told her she would do an errand and then come to the school in about half an hour.

"Well, first we..." Shira began and quickly filled him in on each step of our investigation.

"And they're all just down there in that room as if waiting for a class to come use them!" Shira concluded.

"But what we would really like to do is call Alma and find out if she was the one who moved them and if so, why?" I added.

"Right, because if she wasn't the one, then we *still* have a mystery that needs solving," Shira insisted.

Rabbi Stein smiled and said, "I can see that this won't wait until tomorrow. Let me see if I can get her phone number." He called down to Anita, but she had probably already left because she didn't answer the extension in the kitchen. Rabbi Stein looked up Anita's personal number and got through to her. A few minutes later, he was dialing Alma's phone number.

"Hello Alma," Rabbi Stein's soft voice greeted, "this is Rabbi Stein calling. I have two young investigators in my office that would like to ask you a few questions. Are you feeling well enough to speak with them for just a few minutes?" He paused for her answer, then said, "Okay, I am going to put you on speaker so we can all hear, is that all right? Fine, then. You will be speaking with two of our students here, Shira and Aviva." He pressed the speaker button and said, "Go ahead girls."

"Hi Alma, this is Shira. I was wondering if, by any chance, you had something to do with moving all the boxes of computers that were in the lunchroom yesterday." There was silence on the other end. I realized there might be a problem.

"It's okay if you did, you're not in trouble or anything," I reassured her. "We just want to know how they all got to the basement. Maybe you were helping out?" I suggested.

"Yes, si," Alma said, "I see all boxes and night before, hear Mr. Juan say they need to be moved to base…base…met? Miss Anita tell me I need to help and not always being told what to do. I come in early and put boxes on cart and move to basement. I work hard!" she told us. "Not wait be told. That what Miss Anita tell me do."

"Beis medrash…base-met…basement!" I mouthed quietly to Shira. She nodded.

Rabbi Stein joined in "I am sure you are a very hard worker, Alma. We aren't upset at your trying to help out. But, I think that Anita would prefer if you ask her about doing such big jobs. Start with doing small things in the kitchen. I think that is what you were hired for, right?"

"Si, Rabbi Stein," Alma agreed. "I ask Miss Anita first, for big things."

"But, Alma, why did you put all the computers on the desks?" I asked her.

"I no do that!" she denied. "I only put all boxes on floor and bring back cart for kitchen."

"Well, okay then. Thank you, Alma, and I hope you feel better," I said.

"Yes, feel better soon," Shira added.

"Thank you, Alma," Rabbi Stein said, "get plenty of rest and call if you are not better by tomorrow."

"I do that. Gracias!" Alma said and hung up.

"She thought Juan said "basement" when what he really said was, "bais medrash," I told Rabbi Stein. He nodded and stroked his beard. "So, young ladies, it appears we still have one piece of the puzzle missing. What do you propose to do about that?"

I sat thinking. Shira fidgeted with a pad that was on the desk, folding and unfolding the top sheet. No one had any ideas.

"Well then, let's go visit this mysterious classroom in the basement," he said with a smile. Shira jumped to her feet, knocking the pad and a few pens to the floor and quickly stooping to put them back. I got up and we all went to the elevator to the basement.

"I didn't even know this was here," Shira told Rabbi Stein as we descended.

"The students are not meant to know about this elevator as it is off limits. No one is supposed to go down there since it isn't always safe and there is no reason to be there." For a minute we felt guilty, but then I remembered, "But you gave us permission to investigate, so we weren't breaking any rules, right?"

"Just in this instance," Rabbi Stein agreed as he stepped from the elevator.

"This way!" Shira said and scooted ahead to lead the way. When we got to the room with the computers, Rabbi Stein peered through the window.

"Those are definitely the computers," he said.

"And look over there, there's the boxes they came in," I said.

Rabbi Stein looked around a moment, then said, "I have an idea about this last puzzle piece. Come with me." He led us past the pillars to the darker side of the basement. Flicking a switch on a pillar, the whole space lit up, revealing huge heating units and pipes and other large cylinders and things I didn't know the use of.

We came to a door that was slightly ajar and Rabbi Stein knocked, "Hello?" he called. A man dressed in overalls stepped to the door.

"Rabbi? What can I do for you?"

"Do you know anything about a stack of computer boxes that were unloaded in room A down here, Rob?"

"Oh, that," the man said, "we had a service guy come to fix the furnace this morning, and he told me that a little tiny bit of a woman was trying to unload all of them all by herself. He asked if he could help her and I told him to go ahead while I checked out his work on the furnace. When he got back, he told me that after the woman left, he saw that the boxes were in front of a classroom and decided he could be a bigger help by unpacking all the computers and setting them up. I didn't realize it until he was done.

"He was trying to help. Evidently, he had a job once where he was the one to set up new computers in a company. I was going to contact you and ask what you wanted me to do with the computers, but then the power to the furnace kept going out and I was on the phone all day resolving the problem and completely forgot about it."

Rabbi Stein grinned and looked at us, "Well, there you have it, girls. The final question answered." We smiled back. "Thank you, Rob. I'll have Juan talk to you about packing these onto carts and bringing them to the computer room as soon as it's ready. In the meantime, we can leave them where they are," Rabbi Stein told him.

"Juan!" Shira breathed. I nodded. "We told Juan we would let him know if we found the computers. He seemed to feel guilty about their disappearance," I explained to Rabbi Stein.

"I'll let him know first thing in the morning and tell him that it was you two who asked that he be told. Come girls, I'll accompany you to the front entrance where your mother should be arriving any minute," he looked at Shira, who looked at her watch and agreed. "We've got five minutes."

We all started back and Rabbi Stein said, "You have both been excellent detectives. Your persistence has saved us a lot of aggravation and paperwork while also recovering valuable property. I am proud of both of you. I'll keep you two in mind whenever we need a mystery solved in the future. If you are interested, you might write this experience up for all the school to read. I'm sure they would enjoy your adventure."

Shira looked doubtful. "Um…I'm not really that good a writer."

"But I am!" I offered. "I can do the writing and you can help me remember all the details and what led to what, right?"

Shira brightened, "Sure, that should be fun! As long as *I'm* not the one doing the writing. I'm more an idea person."

I laughed. "You sure are!"

Just then Shira's mother drove up. Rabbi Stein leaned in through the passenger window and told her, "Your daughter is a very observant and persistent young lady. Together with her keenly intelligent friend, Aviva, they will go on in life, with Hashem's help, to accomplish wonderful things. I'm sure they will fill you in on their adventure!"

"Why, thank you Rabbi," Mrs. Markowitz said with pleased surprise.

"Thank you, girls. See you tomorrow." Rabbi Stein closed the car door after we climbed in and waved us off.

Shira *has* become my friend, I thought bemusedly. I guess I learned firsthand that you really do have to look deeper to see who a person is. All that stuff that made me think badly of her didn't really matter. It was all outside stuff. Stuff that gets in the way of really liking and accepting someone. I thought I could now really *get* yesterday's lesson deep inside. *Love your neighbor as yourself.* I'm not perfect. Neither is Shira. But she has so many cool aspects to her.

That night, as I related the day's experience to my family over dinner, I realized something that gave me a feeling of excitement that rushed from my toes to my head. By telling them all the good things about Shira, I was actually able to see her in a completely different way. I knew exactly what I would write on my V'ahavta paper.

The next day, when the classes gathered for their Middah of the Month shmuz, we each held a paper with a list of positive things we'd thought of about our partner. I had decorated mine with vines and flowers all around the edges, with "Shira" written in fancy letters across the top. Mrs. Klein put on some soft background music and told us to exchange our papers with our partners. I handed mine to Shira and took the page she handed me, but I couldn't concentrate on it. My entire focus was on watching Shira read the page I had handed her. Her face transformed from slightly worried to the biggest, most beautiful smile. She looked at me and just grinned. I don't think I had ever felt so good in my life. I didn't even think to read my own paper until I realized I was still just holding it. Shira, as she had confessed to Rabbi Stein, was a *not* a good writer, or speller.

I looked down and saw three lines with these words: *Grate ideas, adventurus and a realy realy good friend to have at your side.* I swallowed and looked back at Shira with a slightly wobbly smile of my own. Yes, we were now friends.

I thought of the words that my friends and I had first laughingly labeled Shira with, and was so very glad I had never, ever written them down. As Shira took a seat beside me, I glanced at her list and realized that, until I had spoken and written the words that described all her good qualities, I didn't realize there were so many more nice things about her than awkward ones. In fact, I really didn't see those any more. So what if she knocked something over? She always picked it up. So what if she asked lots of questions? They had a really observant mind behind them. I almost never gave her a chance.

And I thought to myself, *that was a close call!*

Ah, Now I See

Having a special needs person in the class made Avner very uncomfortable. He was different and weird—wasn't he?

I didn't want to see him. Didn't want to hear him. But no sooner than I had settled into my seat did I hear the tap, tap, tapping of his stick. It was Ben, the new boy in our class. The new *blind* boy, tapping and shuffling his feet and feeling his way to his seat by the door. I squirmed a bit in my chair and looked down at my desk. I didn't know why Ben's half-open eyes and different ways made me so uncomfortable. They just did.

On the first day of seventh grade, both the principal and our rebbi, Rabbi Teichman, spoke to us about what it meant to have this special needs boy in our classroom. They told us that the new boy was just like any other seventh grader, except that he could not see. Instead of using his eyes to find his way, he used a stick that he could tap on things and "see" where he was going. He used special equipment to take notes and read assignments. The rebbeim told us that we should welcome Ben to our class and treat him with kindness, and help him whenever he asked for help. Mostly, they told us, just make sure you talk to him in a friendly way, just as you would any other new kid. Since he could not see body language like smiling or shrugging or holding out a hand for a friendly slap, we had to remember to talk to him and tell him who we were and what we thought or felt.

How do you do that? I wondered. When my friend Shmulie first came into our class in third grade, we immediately hit it off just by grinning at the same pranks and jokes, making a few faces and realizing we had the same sense of humor. We didn't talk about being friends, we just were.

Most of the kids were pretty friendly toward Ben, going up to him and introducing themselves and joking a bit with him. That first day, I tried. Feeling very awkward, I went up to him at lunch.

"Hi," I said, "um, my name is Avner...er...Avner Schwartz. I sit in the first row opposite your desk." I didn't know what else to say. Ben appeared to be looking down, his eyes half closed as if he was shy, but he said, "Nice to meet you, Avner! What do you like to do?"

"Uh, well, mostly I read and I'm pretty good at basketball..." I shut my mouth, horrified. How could I be so dumb? This boy couldn't read and couldn't play games because he couldn't see them. I felt really bad for him and really embarrassed about telling him about things he couldn't relate to. Before he could say another word, I blurted, "Well, I gotta run, see you!" and took off, slapping my forehead in exasperation. Why did I say that? See you? He can't see me and he can't know if I see him. I felt so dumb. He's just so different from me, I thought. We have nothing in common.

Some of the other kids seemed to have figured out how to talk to a blind kid. Yaakov, who sat two rows over from Ben, seemed the most comfortable with him. Because our class was a bit rowdy and quick, there was usually a lot of jostling and bumping in the hallways getting to and from our classrooms. On some days Yaakov would guide Ben to and from our classroom door, holding his arm so Ben didn't need to use his walking stick. Once in the room, though, Ben did most things by himself. He had an electronic braille note-taking device that actually seemed pretty cool. I realized after a while that he could read using braille, and also could listen to audio books. He was talking to Yaakov about the book I had just finished last night.

One day, three weeks before Chanukah, Rabbi Teichman made an exciting announcement. "Boys, this year, I'll be holding a Chanukah raffle. Everyone who memorizes a full daf (page) of Gemara will receive ten dollars as Chanukah gelt and be entered into a drawing. The three winners of the drawing will come to my house for a Chanukah party to celebrate and light the menorah with my family." Rebbi winked and said, "Come with empty stomachs. There will be lots of good food."

We all looked at each other and grinned. We had all heard about Rebbetzin Teichman's delicious latkes. She made them from scratch, and they were said to be mouthwateringly delicious. This year we were learning Bava Metzia. I was fairly good at memorizing and was pretty sure I would be entered into the raffle. I hoped that my good buddies, Shaya and Avrami, and I would win. I looked around and noticed that Ben was grinning with the same happy anticipation that the rest of the class showed. I secretly hoped that if I won, he would not be one of the other contest winners. He wouldn't get our jokes about things like cafeteria food, such as the rice the cafeteria called pilaf but the kids called pea laugh because it was green and kind of clumpy. We would have to watch everything we said and couldn't talk about things he wouldn't understand because of his blindness. What if we embarrassed him?

A week later, Rabbi Teichman came to class ready to hear us recite our memorized Gemara portion, one by one. I aced it! Two-thirds of our class got put into the raffle, Ben included. Rabbi Teichman told the boys who didn't make it that he knew that everyone in this class had the ability to memorize a daf and if they put a little more effort into it, they could do it. We would be having a different kind of raffle before Pesach and they were welcome to try again.

Rebbi began to pull the names of those in the raffle out of a lunch bag. "Our first winner is…Shaya Cooper!" The class clapped and Shaya let out a loud, "YES!" "Next is…Ben Schulman!" Ben's grin was wide as he bobbed his head and said softly, "Can't wait for those latkes!"

"And lastly…Avner Schwartz!" I won.

"Wow! That's me!" I called out. My best friend, Shaya, the new boy and I were all going to Rebbi's house for the fifth night of Chanukah. I had mixed feelings now, though. On the one hand, I was happy to have won. On the other hand, I was a little disappointed about Ben coming along. I mean, how would we even play dreidel? He couldn't even tell if the dreidel landed on a gimmel or a nun. The truth was, he just made me feel uncomfortable and sorry for him. I didn't like the feeling.

The fifth day of Chanukah arrived. At lunch, Shaya and I sat together, and talked about how we would get to Rabbi

Teichman's house. Just then, Ben came tap tapping his way over to our table.

"Can I catch a ride with one of you?" he asked.

I don't know what got into me, but I said, in a real friendly tone, "Sure, Ben, my father is picking Shaya up at 5:45. Can we get you at 5:50?" Ben nodded, smiling. He told us he would need help down his stairs, as the ground was a bit icy and his parents would not be home at that time. The next day we pulled up in front of Ben's house at exactly 5:50p.m. He was waiting on his front porch with his stick. I met him at the top of the stairs and greeted him nervously. What if Ben would fall while I helped him?

"Let me hold your arm, and just walk normally," he said. "I'll be able to feel where to go with my cane." His voice calmed me down. We walked to Dad's car and rode to Rebbi's house. When we arrived, Rebbi, his wife, their ten-year-old son, and two-year-old twin boys greeted us at the door.

"Just in time, boys. Come in, we were just getting ready to light my great-grandfather's menorah. Isn't it beautiful?" And with that, Rebbi lit the shamash and recited the prayers, then lit the five wicks that floated in the olive oil cups. We all sang Maoz Tzur together. It really sounded beautiful with Rabbi Teichman's son singing harmony and Ben's surprisingly strong tenor making all our voices blend together.

Our rebbi introduced us to the rebbetzin, his son, Aryeh, and his twin toddlers, Noam and Nosson. "This is Ben Schulman, Shaya Cooper, and Avner Schwartz, all winners of this year's raffle. We can play dreidel later, but for now, we are in for a treat! Rebbetzin's delicious latkes, fresh off the stove!" We left the family room and the flickering lights of the silver menorah and I, feeling more comfortable, led Ben by his arm to the dining room table. Shaya followed, holding a toddler by each hand. I was looking at the pile of crispy brown latkes and absentmindedly started to sit—in the same seat Ben had started sitting in.

"Hey, get your own seat, mister!" he quipped. "I don't think either of us is skinny enough to share," he added with an impish grin.

"Well, who says this was *your* chair?" I answered back without much thought, "Maybe it was *my* chair that you're sitting in."

"Nope, I'm the one that pulled it out first, so it's mine, so scoot!" I laughed and shrugged, then remembered and said, "Okay, I'll take this other chair that, for your information, has a cushier seat, so, your loss."

"Just as long as I get my share of latkes," Ben retorted. "They sure smell delicious!"

"The best in town!" Shaya chimed in.

"Certainly *my* favorites!" Rebbi said with a big smile, "Please help yourselves. There's plenty of applesauce and sour cream to go with them, so let's eat!" And with that, we all began piling our plates, making our brachos and eating. I discovered that all I had to do was put the platter near Ben, say, "Eleven o'clock, platter; four o'clock, serving fork," and he was able to feel his way to the edge of the platter and spear some latkes for himself.

"Want some of this applesauce or sour cream?" I asked Ben.

"Applesauce would be fine. If you can put it at three o'clock on my plate for me, that would be great." I did so and didn't feel strange at all. Just friendly. It was even kind of fun. So what if

Ben used the tip of a finger on his left hand to feel the latkes on his plate so he could cut them? Some of the other kids were using their fingers as well. After devouring about five latkes, I noticed something odd. Ben had lifted his head up from his plate. He was sniffing.

"Oh no!" he exclaimed suddenly.

"What's wrong?" Rebbi asked.

"I smell smoke!"

"I don't smell anything," I said nonchalantly. But Rebbi frowned, "Are you sure it's not my wife's cooking oil? Sometimes the last few pancakes get a little well done, leaving a bit of a burnt smell."

"I don't smell anything," added Shaya, "can you please pass me more latkes?"

"No, this is serious!" Ben was frantic. "Something is burning! Rabbi Teichman, check the menorah!"

Rabbi Teichman ran into the family room where, indeed, he saw that one of the curtains had slipped out of its restraint and caught on fire.

"Help, Rebbetzin, bring me our fire extinguisher!" The rebbetzin quickly brought over the extinguisher, then announced, "Everyone, follow me!" She grabbed a toddler under each arm and led us out toward the side porch. Shaya immediately took one of the twins from her while I grabbed Ben's arm and led him through the side door and down the stairs.

"Come on, Aryeh, walk with us," I called as Aryeh stayed on the top stair trying to see inside.

From the lawn outside, we could see Rebbi through the window, extinguishing the fire that fortunately had only partially burned one of the white lace curtains. Rebbi joined us outside and used his cellphone to call the fire department.

"Better make sure everything is safe and that there are no lingering embers," he explained.

"Funny, I didn't smell anything," Shaya exclaimed. "Ben, how did you smell it?"

"I have a more developed sense of smell. Because I'm blind, I've learned to use my other senses more fully than other people. They help draw a picture of what is going on around me. I'm often the first one to smell, and even to hear things."

"Well, you certainly saved my home, and my entire family," Rabbi Teichman said. "Because you smelled the fire so soon, there was hardly any damage." He grasped Ben's hand. "Thank you so much! Hashem certainly has blessed you with a fine talent—and the strength and confidence to insist when everyone else thought it was nothing."

On the lawn that night, standing with Rebbi and his family, Shaya and Ben, I thought about how strange it was that my feelings and attitude had completely changed. Before, I had wanted to run away from Ben. I had thought him strange and completely different from "normal" kids. Now I knew that Ben was just a regular kid who could goof around and be like any other seventh grader. But Ben was also an extraordinary person. Because he couldn't see with his eyes, he had developed a stronger sense of smell and hearing. Hashem, in His infinite kindness and wisdom, had allowed him to "see" with his other senses. And tonight, on the fifth night of Chanukah, for the first time, *I* saw. I saw things in a new way—as if with a different sense. Kinda like Ben. Instead of feeling sorry for Ben, I had plenty to learn from him. I felt like a different person: someone who could learn from a kid who wasn't less than me, only different.

Catching On

When Michoel is asked to go with his father to deliver to the poor, he thinks it's a waste of time. Hanging out with friends seems so much more fulfilling...until he discovers the hidden perks.

I didn't want to go, but my dad insisted it was important.

"What's the big deal about me giving some old poor people a few bags of food?" I grumbled. My friend, Gabe, had invited me over for the afternoon to jam on our guitars together. That sounded like a lot more fun than making deliveries to some crummy old houses.

But once my dad told me I had to do something, I knew there was no arguing with it. Usually he had a good reason, but I couldn't see how my helping him do what he was already doing anyway would do any good.

My dad was working with a group called Ahavas Yisroel to deliver meals to people who were too poor or too old to get it for themselves.

"Grab that box, Michoel, and bring it to the car," called my dad as he headed out the door with a large carton of food. I sighed and grabbed the box and followed him to the truck he was driving for deliveries. I sat in silence as we drove to the first drop-off. Maybe this wouldn't take too long and I could still make it to Gabe's.

We got out, and parked, and I looked up the four steps to study the house. It looked pretty ordinary, with an old bicycle lying on the somewhat weedy lawn and a few toys scattered here and there.

"Here," Dad said, giving me a box and taking one himself. We walked up to the door and Dad knocked. A woman answered the door.

"Yes?" she asked. She had a toddler in her arms who was sucking his thumb. He was dressed in a t-shirt and diaper, even though it was not that warm. A little boy who looked about three years old was hanging on to the woman's skirt, peeking out from behind it. He was barefoot and the floor was old linoleum. Wasn't he cold? I ducked my chin down a bit further into my coat collar.

"Delivery!" Dad said with a smile.

"Oh!" the woman stepped back a bit, "please come in and put the boxes in the kitchen!" She didn't smile, but she followed us into the kitchen where my dad put his box on a small table. The kids just stared at us without making a sound. An open jar of peanut butter was on the table with a rice cake on each of five plates. I looked around and saw an open pantry with four shelves. One shelf had a box of salt, a bag of sugar, a box of crackers, a bag of rice, three boxes of pasta and two cans of tomato sauce. That was it. The other shelves were empty. Weird. We had so much stuff on our pantry shelves that we barely knew what we had.

"This should do it until next week," I heard my dad saying.

"I don't know what we would do without your help," the woman said. "Thank you! Baruch Hashem for organizations like Ahavas Yisroel!"

"Let's go Michoel." Dad started walking out and I followed. As I reached the door, I heard a happy squeal and the woman's voice saying, "Chicken *and* fish! Look Yossi, apples! And…" her voice faded as we closed the door and went back to the car.

Who gets all excited about chicken and fish and apples? That's just normal food. But it made me think. Our next stop was at an apartment building. We each took our boxes and Dad buzzed the name on his list.

"Ahavas Yisroel!" he called when the voice came from the speaker asking who was there.

When we came to the door it was already standing open. There was a girl who looked a bit younger than me standing at the door waiting for us. She smiled and opened the door wider for us to enter.

"Hi Mr. Berkowitz!" she said brightly, "guess what?"

"What?" my dad asked as we set the boxes down in the kitchen.

"I got an "A" on my English paper! But now I have to stay home to help Mommy with the new baby so I might not have time to do the next one so well," she finished all in a rush.

"An "A" takes a lot of work," my dad nodded, "and I'm sure you will be a big help to your mother and the new baby. Is he cute?"

The girl made a face. "Nah. He's funny looking. But I love him anyway. Mommy says he'll grow into his face. I think that means he'll look better when he gets a bit older."

"All he does is cry, sleep and poop!" said a voice from the other side of the room. I hadn't noticed a kid a few years older than me kinda sprawled over an ugly green recliner. There were tears at the seams with white stuffing poking out here and there.

"That's what babies do," answered my dad as we set our boxes down in their kitchen. "You did the same thing when you were a baby."

"Not me," the boy denied, "I was playing with balls from the get go, just ask my dad." He was picking at some threads in a hole in his sock. When he noticed me looking, he tucked his foot under the cushion. "I'm gonna be a great basketball player. My rebbi says he's never seen anyone shoot baskets like I can!" he ended proudly.

"Well, then, you keep practicing and I'm sure you'll be star material," Dad said. "But I don't think your new brother will be ready to shoot baskets with you quite yet," he joked. "Give him a few years to get his feet under him, huh?" The boy smiled a bit, but I noticed that he was staring at my shoes. My practically new Air Jordan sneakers.

"Who's he?" the boy asked.

"This is my son, Michoel. Michoel, meet Aryeh and Shoshi," my dad nodded his head to each of the kids.

"Hi guys," I tried to smile, but it just wouldn't come.

"See you next week," my dad said.

We turned to go out the door and Dad stopped and looked over his shoulder. "There are some perishables in those cartons that need to go in the fridge," he told them. I saw that the kid's shoes were all lined up near the door. There was a ratty old pair of high tops there that looked about my size.

"We'll take care of it Mr. Berkowitz," the girl answered, "see you next week!"

"Dad, did you see their house?" I asked as we drove to the next stop. "Everything looked really shabby. Michoel's socks even had holes in them. I mean, not just one like I sometimes get near my toes, but lots of them."

"Yes, Michoel, they are in a very difficult place right now and barely have enough to get by. That is why we brought them food."

"But, doesn't their dad work? I know the mom just had a baby, but if they need more money, didn't she have a job?"

"They both work, Michoel, but they just don't make enough right now to make ends meet," Dad said. "Sometimes you do everything you can, but you still need a little help until things turn around for you. The father is just finishing studying for his CPA tests, which will let him be an accountant. Most of the places that would hire him will only do so if he has passed those tests. So, for now he is working in a restaurant until he can get a better job. The mom is a teacher. They don't make enough to pay for rent, tuition, their car and insurance, and still have enough for decent food."

I sat silently thinking. You could work hard and still not have enough? People in our own neighborhood didn't have food to eat?

Our next stop was at the home of two very old ladies. Their faces were all lines that crinkled and went up when they smiled and welcomed us. They asked if we would stay and have tea with them. Dad told them we had more deliveries to make and the food would spoil if we stayed. I guessed that they might have trouble with moving all the groceries, because Dad started unloading them and putting the cold items in their fridge and the other items on their shelves.

"Ooh, look, Miriam!" exclaimed the one with the pinkish, fluffy hair, "We have biscuits for our tea and soft bread and honey! We'll feast tonight!"

The other lady clapped her hands and smiled, "Honey! And look! Soup! Let's heat some up right now!"

"Yes! We'll eat that with these crackers," the other answered, eagerly taking a box of crackers Dad had just put on their counter. They were busy getting out pots and plates as we quietly walked out the door. They were so involved in getting things ready that they forgot to say, "thank you." But then, it felt like maybe their happy excitement was more thank you than any words.

When Dad pulled up for our next stop, I couldn't believe it. The house was big and fancy with pillars on the porch at the front door and fancy designs cut into the two glass panels beside it. When we rang the bell, it chimed a pretty tune. The woman who answered the door was dressed like my mom would dress for Shabbos or a fancy dinner. She was wearing high heels and had jewelry on, but she did not look happy.

"Thank you so much!" she breathed as we brought in our boxes. "Just put them on the dining room table and I'll take care of them." We walked in past a fancy little table in the entryway and turned into a very large dining room with a sparkly chandelier hanging above a long table. I counted twenty-four chairs. Wow! They must have lots of company. I could see the kitchen through the dining room archway. It was really big, with two sinks and two ovens and everything spotless and shiny.

"There're another two boxes in the car," my dad told the woman. "We'll be right back with them." *More boxes?* I didn't get it.

Outside, my dad handed me another large box while he pulled out an even larger one for himself.

"Uh, Dad? Aren't these people rich?" Dad did his right eyebrow lift. That meant he was listening and waiting for me to go on. "I mean, look at this house! It's big! The furniture is fancy! The lady is fancy! Why would they need stuff from Ahavas Yisroel?"

Dad smiled. "Let's bring this stuff in and then we can talk in the car," he suggested. So we carried everything into the house. I stopped in shock. There must have been twenty-five kids lined up from the boxes to the kitchen, and spread around the island in the center. And it was noisy! At first I could only hear a loud babble, but soon it became clearer.

"Milk. Perishable. Fridge stop!" called a curly haired boy of about twelve. He had pulled a gallon milk jug out of a box and practically threw it to the next kid in line. The milk got handed down the line from kid to kid until the one standing in front of the fridge got it and put it inside. While this was going on the curly haired one had called out, "Pasta! Top shelf!" He tossed two bags to the kid at the end of the table, who repeated the instruction and passed them on to a kid who stood about three feet away, who passed it on to the next one. By then the curly haired one had called out, "Tomato sauce, pantry, slider!" and passed four cans on. Since each kid in line repeated the instructions, there was a lot of noise. But items were moving down what I now realized were two spaced out lines and getting put away neatly where they belonged. It looked like some kind of comedy show. Every so often a kid in the kitchen would say something like, “bulk size intervention!” and a big kid would run up and take the large bag of sugar…or flour or something and run off with it to a closet in the corner.

I didn’t realize I was grinning until I met my father’s eyes, and saw the answering grin on his face. Just then the woman who had first greeted us walked into the room and smiled a kind of tired smile at us.

“Thank you so much!” she said. “This should keep us for a bit, if I can get them to stop eating for … oh, say an hour or two.”

Dad laughed. “Just give me a call if you run low on something. We have you on priority list,” he had to practically shout to be heard, but the woman nodded contentedly and we headed out with a wave.

“Wow, Dad!” I breathed, “What is that place? Some kind of boys’ home or something?”

“The Kleins were once a very well-off family and when their own children were grown and moved out, Mrs. Klein began fostering Jewish kids who needed a place to live and grow in a warm, frum environment. Somehow, people heard about her and it grew from taking one or two kids in to…well, you saw. The Kleins are wonderful people who really care about those kids. But they lost most of their money in some deal that was not their fault, and now they barely have the funds to support themselves, let alone those children. Ahavas Yisroel stepped in to make it possible for all those kids to have a happy home to stay in, and for the Kleins to continue loving and guiding all of them. The house is big enough. We just make sure they have enough for food and clothing.”

"Wow!" I breathed. After a moment I looked at him and asked, "Hey, Dad, what do you think Mom would say if we tossed our groceries to each other to put them away?"

"Don't even go there," he said straight-faced. Then he looked at me and I looked at him...and we both dissolved in laughter.

By the time we got home, I was feeling both tired and strangely satisfied. My head was full of the things I had seen. At dinner I described the homes we had visited to my mother and Josh and Elisheva, my brother and sister. When I spoke about the home with the assembly line put away, Josh piped up with, "Could we...?" But Mom interjected a firm, "No!" before he could even finish.

"It's really wonderful what the Kleins have done with their home!" Mom said. "And I'm glad you were able to help your father today. Do you realize he got back an hour earlier than last Sunday? I think you must have been a big help!"

I ducked my head and murmured, "I guess it was okay." Mom smiled and exchanged a look with my Dad.

"I was happy for his help," Dad said.

"Can I come with you next time?" Josh asked. "I'd like to see that house with all those kids. What a circus!"

"No. This is not a show. Ahavas Yisroel is about how we can help each other become stronger and kinder. If you have an idea how to do that, then I will be happy to listen," he looked questioningly at Josh, who nodded in understanding.

The next Sunday after lunch I was ready to go with my dad when he drove up with the AY truck. I was wearing my old, comfy sneakers and jumped up into the truck, stuffing a paper bag on the floor by my feet. This Sunday we stopped at a few other homes, one of them that seemed just like ours, but I guess the people there were having a hard time and needed the help. It made me think that anyone could need help. Even, I guessed, my family. I closed my eyes for a minute and thanked Hashem for taking care of my family and giving us what we needed.

When we got to Aryeh and Shoshi's house, I grabbed the paper bag and stuck it on top of my box and brought everything into the house.

"Hey, Michoel," greeted Shoshi. "Wanna see my new baby brother?"

"Sure!" I nodded. She put her finger to her mouth in a shushing motion and led me to a basinet in the living room. The baby was making sucking motions with his mouth and was really tiny. He looked about the size of my football, all wrapped tightly in a blanket.

"Isn't he adorable?" she asked. "He doesn't look so squished any more.

"Um. I guess. He's got really tiny hands," I offered. Shoshi nodded and looked satisfied.

"Thanks for the delivery," she said. "We really need the help right now but my dad says he has a line on a new job and if he gets it we should be up on our feet in no time, which means probably at least six months to a year, but at least we'll be doing better, Baruch Hashem!"

Boy, she sure could say a lot in one sentence. But I liked her friendly, open way.

"Gotta go, Michoel," my dad called.

"Oh, wait." I ran over to the box I had brought in and pulled out the paper bag. Give this to Aryeh, okay?" I told Shoshi. "Tell him they pinched my toes. See you!" and with that I ran out the door to catch up with my dad.

Once in the truck, Dad looked over at me and raised that eyebrow.

"Your new shoes?" he asked.

"He needed them more than I did, Dad. These will last for a long while yet. Mom just got the Jordans for me 'cause I wanted them for my birthday. I didn't really *need* them."

My dad reached over and shook my hand. He didn't say another word. We finished our deliveries and I knew that I would never again complain about not doing what *I* wanted on a Sunday. And I no longer looked at the people we delivered to as weird, creepy or different. Just...regular people who needed a little help.

Fun & Facts

Ayin Tovah - עין טובה

Looking with a Good Eye and Seeing the Whole Person

Seeing with an ayin tovah—a good eye—is another way of saying one should look at things with a positive attitude, and find the good in a person or situation.

Developing an ayin tovah, an eye that looks at and for the good, is really important. When we train ourselves to look at the world through the ayin tovah that is within us, we get the blessing of seeing beyond the surface. We see what is really important and beautiful in the world. We also get to recognize the wonderful fact that Hashem made everything—just as it was meant to be.

Cool Fact:

Sometimes we look at a person's physical disability or deformity and automatically assume that the person is weak or not as capable as we are. But there are also internal disabilities that we cannot see from the outside. These disabilities prove just as much a challenge as the outer ones. At times we might see a person behaving in a strange or different way and think they are just odd. We make assumptions about them, not knowing that they cannot help it, that they are doing the best they can with their disability. For example, some kids get extremely nervous in crowds. Some children can't read because their brains don't see words and letters the usual way. Others have trouble recognizing their physical boundaries or can't seem to keep things in order. They might knock things over, bump into other kids, or have extremely messy backpacks, lockers and rooms.

WHOA! Wait a minute. Everyone is different. We are not all alike.

We all have strengths and weaknesses. To get along with others, we really need to focus on their strengths. Perhaps the person who is hyperactive is stronger, more outgoing, and even more successful in life than someone without any challenges. And, just maybe, that loud person is very generous, and the next time you need to borrow a pen and paper, or share a lunch when you forgot your own, he will be the one who is there for you. And that kid in the wheelchair? She might be the smartest kid in the class. Look for the positive, and you will find it.

External Challeges:

Interview: A seventh grader's tale.

Here's how one middle schooler with an obvious, *external* challenge, learned to see himself with an ayin tovah:

Elazar is a seventh grader with whom we spoke, who told us some of the difficulties he faced having a right hand that had only two fingers: a thumb and pointer. He said that three of his fingers were caught in a window when he was two and had to be removed. He learned to write with both hands and do most heavy things, like lift his backpack and use a hammer, with his left hand.

"The worst part," he told us, "is how people react to my two-fingered hand. When I was little, kids refused to hold my hand, like for circle time or taking walks. I guess it creeped them out. Then, when I was in kindergarten and was paired up with someone for a project, kids often refused to be my partner because they were so uncomfortable seeing my hand doing whatever thing we were working on."

"How did that make you feel?" we asked.

"At first, I really didn't understand what the problem was. I mean, it was just the way I was. But as I got a little older, I became very self-conscious about my hand and kept it in my pocket or in a fist whenever I could. I used my left hand for everything: eating, writing, holding things. I was embarrassed whenever someone got a glimpse of my hand. I started to feel something was wrong with me and that I wasn't as good as other people. I just felt sad and generally ucky.

"Sometimes I would get angry that I had this half-hand and wished I could be normal like other kids." Elazar shrugged. "Now, I realize that everyone has something they have to deal with, and missing a few fingers isn't the worst thing. It hasn't prevented me from doing anything so far. I even play guitar. I can't do it like someone with ten fingers, but I don't need to. I do it my way. I strum with my right hand and use a pick when I need to and everyone says my playing is really good."

"Do you still feel embarrassed when people see your hand?" we asked.

"Only when people act weird when they see it," he said. "If they look and then just go on as if everything is normal, then I am fine. But if they make a face or look away or act nervous, it brings back all those feelings of not being as good or having something wrong with me. I mean, I know missing fingers is not how it's supposed to be. It's not the norm. But for *me* it *is* normal. I am normal."

"You certainly are," we agreed.

We thanked Elazar for sharing his story with us. What we see on the outside is not who a person is, and with Elazar, that comes across quite clearly.

Internal Challenges:

Now let's meet some kids who have some *hidden* difficulties. We might not see their challenges at first, but here's a list of a few to keep in mind. Remember, it's not up to us to judge how they are doing. It is up to us to treat each other with dignity and kindness, no matter how they behave. We need to look at others with a good eye—with kindness and tolerance, accepting their differences. That is how Hashem looks at us, and we want to emulate Him in every way.

Every person does the best that he or she can with the tools that Hashem has provided. Our attitude should be one that seeks to be helpful, not critical.

Let's learn from Psychologist Dr. Cindy Sandler, who can explain more:

Memory: *When our teacher tells us to open our books to page 40 and finish the two-step word problems, why does Shimon open his book and sit there looking confused?*

Some kids have trouble remembering directions that require more than one step. The teacher might have to repeat things for them, giving one instruction at a time. We shouldn't judge them and certainly not make fun of them. This is how Hashem wired their brains to work. Often, they are talented in some area such as art or music or writing.

Difficulty Maintaining Attention**:** *When Sara begins to hum while working on her English assignment, why does Talya get up from her seat and yell, "Be quiet!" Others can barely hear Sara. Her humming doesn't seem to bother anyone but Talya.*

Some kids are easily distracted. While a soft noise might not bother most kids, some have a hard time tuning out distractions and staying focused. A soft humming that is not part of the lesson will frustrate such a person as he or she tries to stay on task—but repeatedly gets distracted by the noise.

Just because most people can ignore the noise doesn't mean that everyone can.

Visual Difficulties: *Whenever the teacher calls on Reuven to read out loud to the class, he reads very slowly and skips words. He's a smart boy, so what's up with him?*

Some kids actually see double when they read, or the letters might appear to move or be turned backwards. These kids are often very smart and often cover up their problem by making jokes or finding inventive ways to keep from having to read in class. Sometimes working with a developmental ophthalmologist or a specialized eye doctor and doing eye exercises can help. Depending on the exact cause of the problem, specialized reading exercises can also help them learn to distinguish the words on a page.

Shyness: *Why does Elisheva look at the ground and remain silent every time somebody asks her a question? She barely says a word. Is she trying to ignore her classmates?*

Elisheva is so nervous about talking to other people that she can't say a word. Someone like this needs others to be patient with them—and extra nice. Don't make fun of them or think that they are being snobby. It's just more difficult for them to feel comfortable with others.

(As per Cindy Ward Sandler, Ph.D. Licensed Psychologist, Columbia, MD)

REMEMBER: Every person has his or her own challenges in life. Some are more visible than others. Our job is to treat others with respect, kindness and care—just like *we* want to be treated.

It's True!

New research has shown that people who are blind from before age 3 really do have heightened abilities in their other senses, particularly hearing, smell and touch. Often their memory and language abilities are also better. Using brain scans, researchers were able to see that the brain had actually changed in the blind people they tested, showing more connections in parts of the brain to the other senses than to the areas involved with seeing.[1]

There is more and more evidence that shows that when one part of the brain isn't being used, such as the part that processes sight, the brain reorganizes itself in a way that strengthens other senses and abilities. This process is known as *cross-modal neuroplasticity.*[2]

It might not mean that a blind person has a truly *better* sense of smell or hearing, but rather that the brain processes the information differently, making the input from those senses clearer, and more noticeable. The end result is *as if* those senses are better.

1 Miller, Sara G. (2017, March 22). *Why Other Senses May Be Heightened in Blind People.* Retrieved from https://www.livescience.com/58373-blindness-heightened-senses.html

2 Rauschecker JP. Compensatory plasticity and sensory substitution in the cerebral cortex. Trends Neurosci. 1995;18:36–43. [PubMed]

Chapter Five

Positive Words

Shmiras Halashon – שמירת הלשון

Guarding One's Speech

From לשון הרע — *Lashon hora*

– Speaking Evil

Tricky Signs

Reuven and Shlomo are both running for class president. Things get tricky when one of them gets bad-mouthed and friends take sides.

Dovid was one of those kids that seem to vibrate with energy. He was full of ideas, a fountain of witty comments, constantly moving and ever creative. While his classmates listened quietly to their teacher's instructions, Dovid took apart his lineup of pens and put them back together in various combinations. One pen top got away from him and went flying over the room, hitting the wall and sliding to the floor. The teacher ignored his activities, but those classmates within sight of his desk were riveted. They watched as he somehow cobbled three pens into a tower, holding them together with widespread fingers. One of the springs popped out, then shot away, softly boinging against the head of a student one seat over. The tower then flew apart, each pen piece soaring in a different direction. Giggles broke out across the room.

"Enough, Dovid," said Mrs. Rothberg calmly, "and no, do not go picking up all those pieces right now. Wait until the bell rings." Somehow, she always kept one step ahead of Dovid, catching him right before a major disturbance. "Why don't you come up here and give out these project sheets?" she directed. "Now, everyone please break up into your work groups and decide how you will tackle this assignment. Dovid, you're working with Asher and Efraim." The two boys exchanged a skeptical glance, but welcomed Dovid into their midst. Disruptive and unpredictable he might be, yet everyone liked Dovid. He was cheerful and friendly and completely oblivious to any negative comments or adverse reactions to his behavior. Unfortunately, staying on task was *not* one of his strong suits. As an idea generator, he shone. Completing a project? Not so much.

Asher and Efraim sat together at lunch, waiting for Dovid to fill his tray and join them so that they could plan their strategy for completing their assignment. Each team had to come up with an idea that they thought would make the world a better place. It could be a technological innovation, a better form of government, a better way to educate, or any other concept that would make things better. The idea had to be at least theoretically possible, be backed by research that showed the need for this innovation, and explain how it would benefit the family, society or the world. Asher was asking Efraim what he thought about an anti-gravity device when Rabbi Stern, the Limudei Kodesh Principal, interrupted their discussion.

"May I have your attention please," he called. The room quickly quieted. Announcements from Rabbi Stern were always interesting. "Today is the official opening of our *You Can Be President* program. Anyone who wishes to run for Student Council President should enter his name on the sign-up sheet outside my office. Please remember that the Student Council President meets with the Student Council once or twice a month to work on devising and planning student activities and mesibas (celebrations.) The responsibilities of the Student President are listed in the pamphlets near the sign-up sheet. Please remember that anyone who runs for President and then becomes President must also keep up with his regular schoolwork. Thank you gentlemen, and remember to campaign on your own merits. Let people know why *you* should be President. Do not speak lashon hora (disrespectful/evil speech) about the other candidates." Rabbi Stern smiled and exited the lunchroom.

The lunchroom instantly filled with the loud buzz of excited voices all speaking at once.

"I'm going to run!" announced Dovid as he plopped his tray down beside the other boys. "I can't wait!"

"Wow!" Efraim's eyes widened. He quickly took a bite of his baked ziti. Asher couldn't decide if his friend was just surprised or disbelieving.

"Yup," continued Dovid excitedly, "I really want to be President. I heard Shlomo say he's gonna run, but I think I can win." Asher and Efraim exchanged a brief look. They didn't doubt that Dovid had the energy necessary for the job. But, against Shlomo?

"Shlomo's the smartest kid in our grade," Efraim said thoughtfully, "it's going to be tough beating him. He doesn't have to take hours to study and can dedicate most of his time to campaigning."

"But he's not as funny as I am, right?" Dovid said, irrepressible as ever. "He doesn't know where the shoes are buried."

"Huh?" "What shoes?" "Whadaya mean, buried?" Efraim and Asher spoke at once, totally confused.

"It's an expression. Like, knowing what's what. But, in this case, taken literally, it would be the shoes of the President that only I can fill because *I* know what it will take to fill them," Dovid said with a conspiratorial double raise of his eyebrows.

Asher rolled his eyes and Efraim shook his head as if to clear it. "Well," he said, "you certainly have a style all your own."

"Yep, and I'll take that style all the way to the Presidency!" Dovid declared. "I'm off to begin my planning. See ya guys!" Having gobbled down his ziti, he took his tray and departed.

"Hey, did I hear correctly?" Raffi, another of their classmates slipped into the empty seat. "Is Dovid really going to run for President of the Student Council?"

"That's what he says," Asher told him. Another student squeezed onto our bench with a full tray: soup, ziti, salad, roll, brownie and milk. Nachum was a tall boy who seemed to need a lot of fuel to fill all that long length.

"I don't think that's such a good idea, him having ADHD and all," Raffi confided, "he can barely sit still two seconds, he calls out in class and he can't stay focused for more than a few minutes. Those aren't good traits for Student Council President."

"ADHD?" asked Efraim, "what's that? He adds in high definition?"

"Very funny," Raffi smirked, "it means someone who calls out without restraint and is fidgety and generally can't control himself. Like Dovid."

"Actually," corrected Asher, "it stands for attention-deficit hyperactivity disorder. People who have it have a harder time focusing on certain things. Some just have that and others also have a need to keep moving. They can be a bit fidgety."

"Well, Raffi, how do you know Dovid has that?" asked Efraim.

"Oh, I heard his brother talking about it on the bus," Raffi informed us. "He was telling Avrumi that he wished Dovid could get his schoolwork done with the same focus as he shoots baskets. He really whooshes those shots. Anyway, we can't vote for someone who has a "disorder" for our President, can we? I certainly won't."

"Yeah," said a boy who was sitting nearby, "Dovid is fun and all, but if he has something *wrong* with him, he isn't gonna make President. Can't vote for a defective," he laughed, "get it? A 'D'... A Defective?" Asher and Efraim didn't find it funny at all. Just then the bell rang, interrupting the conversation and calling everyone back to class. Efraim walked with Asher.

"How do you know so much about ... what was it, ADDH?" asked Efraim as they approached their classroom.

"My cousin has it. ADHD. He talks about it a lot. He doesn't have the patience to focus on anything that takes too long if he isn't really interested in it. But, when he *is* into something, he can be uber focused. My cousin can beat me at any computer game and is a whiz at Photoshop and some other programs he uses to make really great posters and brochures for his school." Efraim thought about that for a while.

"Then, if he really wants to be President, he might actually be good at it, right?" he asked as both boys slipped into their seats.

"Yep, possibly," Asher answered, "but Shlomo would also be a really good choice. He's really smart, he's really together and always has a plan. But, what makes my stomach feel all queasy inside is all the negative talk about Dovid. It's lashon hora. I'm worried about how this will hurt him. Not just as a possible candidate, but as a person."

"Yeah, those guys really had me squirming, making fun of his ADHD like that," agreed Efraim. "We don't make fun of people. But it's really hard to discuss who would make a better President without overstepping into lashon hora. I mean, Dovid *is* scattered and he *doesn't* have a lot of control in things like calling out. Those aren't the best traits to represent the school." The teacher walked into the room and the conversation was suspended.

The boys did not have time to discuss the matter any further. A week passed and Asher asked Dovid how his campaigning was going.

"I'm putting up posters tomorrow," he said happily, "it's the first day we're allowed to put them up. *And* I'm halfway done with my speech." Asher looked at Dovid's happy face and realized that he admired Dovid's dedication and effort. Dovid really cared about this. Asher thought that those qualities would make a fine Student Council President and resolved to vote for Dovid.

Sure enough, the next day the school was papered with posters and signs. One was a large, bright red and yellow one that read, "Vote for Dovid—Student Council President." The letters were written neatly with bold outlines and there was a big, yellow smiley face at the bottom. Another read, "Shlomo, #1 for President!" The sign was in black and white bold letters that looked very dramatic. Two other students had signs up as well. Everywhere one turned, students were discussing whom they wanted to vote for. Asher spotted Efraim in the crush and the two were soon together. Efraim told Asher his thoughts about voting for Dovid.

"I'm really sorry to say that I don't think he will have a fair chance at winning," Asher told Efraim. "I've heard too many kids repeating the things we heard about ADHD and how it would affect Dovid's ability to be a good Student Council President."

"I'm not really clear on how we're supposed to decide between candidates *without* speaking lashon hora," Efraim confessed. "I mean, how do you say why someone isn't going to be as good as another without talking about them? Isn't *any* kind of talking about a person a kind of lashon hora? Rechilus or something?" The bell rang and the boys went to class.

Later on that day, the two spoke about this very difficult problem. How do you decide who would be better without lashon hora being a factor? Lashon hora hurts. It embarrasses and degrades people. It makes them feel bad about themselves, sometimes in a way that lasts their entire lives. It could also deprive someone of something he could be good at, like the Student Council President, without good reason.

"I remember when my little sister came home in tears because one of the other girls said she had a crooked walk," Asher told Efraim. "She doesn't really, but her shoes were hurting her that day and she was kind of walking funny. Other girls who heard started making fun of her. Lashon hora is...is ... hora-ble!"

"Good one," said Efraim, "but, what can we do?" How can we stop this?"

"I think we should go talk to Rebbi and ask him. There has to be a way to talk about the pros and cons of someone running for President without it being lashon hora."

The boys told their Rebbi that they needed to speak with him, and he agreed to meet with them during the break after Gemara the following day. Efraim worried about the problem of lashon hora all through dinner. He didn't want to discuss it with his parents until after he got advice from his rebbi, because his rebbi knew exactly what was acceptable for what was going on in school. All that worrying must have exhausted him, because he fell asleep as soon as his head hit the pillow.

When Efraim walked into the school the next day, he was shocked when he saw Dovid's sign. Someone had used black marker to deface it. It now read:

Don't
Vote for Dovid
or You'll Get an ADHD
for Class President

Some kids were pointing at the sign and laughing. Efraim checked Shlomo's sign, but it still looked the same: "Shlomo: #1 for President." He looked around for Asher and spotted him walking to his locker.

"Hey, Asher, did you see what someone did to Dovid's poster?"

"No, what happened?" he asked as he took out his books.

"Come see for yourself!" Efraim grabbed Asher's sleeve and pulled him along. Asher stared up at the sign.

"That's disgusting!" Asher fumed. "Who could have done this?"

"Don't know, but we've got to do something, quick!" But it was too late already. From behind them they heard a guttural cry. "No-o-o!" Both swung around to witness Dovid staring at his poster, a shocked look on his face. Eyes wild and staring, he ripped the poster from the wall and ran into their first period classroom with Mrs. Bernstein. The boys followed Dovid into class and saw their teacher looking at the sign and talking with Dovid. Dovid was sitting rigidly with his head down. Mrs. Bernstein looked angrily at the class.

"Someone," she said sternly, "has been spreading lashon hora." The room stilled as the boys gave their teacher full attention. Efraim looked around to see how the other boys were reacting. Did anyone look guilty? He saw Raffi looking down at his hands as he fiddled with something nervously. Wasn't he the one who had told us about Dovid's ADHD?

Mrs. Bernstein continued, "Not only did someone ruin Dovid's campaign sign by writing ugly words and defacing his property, but now people have negative and hurtful information about Dovid in their minds. This can ruin his chances of becoming Student Council President. It is a truly horrible form of lashon hora and also a form of bullying. You need to admit to the wrong you have done. You need to take responsibility and make it right..."

Efraim couldn't hear the words any longer. He saw Dovid's shoulders heave silently. He was crying. Efraim's hands were two tight fists; he felt his nails pressing into his palms. *This* is what happens when lashon hora is left to splash its dirt on everything, he thought. He felt responsible. He felt terrible. Mrs. Bernstein's gaze passed over the class and stopped on him. *I didn't do it. I like Dovid. I was planning to vote for him,* he yelled in his head. Mrs. Bernstein's mouth was moving, but Efraim could not seem to hear her over the ringing in his ears.

Take responsibility...make it right kept repeating over and over in his head. The ringing grew louder and more insistent, and suddenly he was lying wide awake in his bed at home. His alarm was ringing. He took a deep, shuddering breath as he realized it had been a dream—just a horrible, this-really-feels-real kind of a dream.

That morning, Efraim walked hesitantly into the school, half expecting to see that Dovid's poster had been transformed to his dreamscape vision. With a heartfelt sigh, he saw that it was just as it should be. When Asher met him at his locker, Efraim told him about the dream.

"We really need to get the scoop on this lashon hora aspect of campaigning from Rebbi," Asher advised. "This is really getting to you. And to me, too. I can't wait until our meeting."

During the break, Asher and Efraim expressed their concerns to their rebbi.

"This is a bit of a complicated problem you are facing," he told them, "but first, it *is* true that spreading information that is harmful to a fellow student is lashon hora. We are going to cover the many rules about not speaking lashon hora next year. For now, though, what you should know is that what you are allowed to discuss is anything that has a direct bearing on whether or not a person is good for the job. If there is something that makes him absolutely unsuitable, that would be okay to talk about as well, except for the fact that in this case your rebbeim and teachers would not let someone run for a position if he were unsuitable.

So, that means that you cannot discuss anything about these students other than what you like about their campaign, what you agree or disagree with when they present their plans for the school, and whether you agree with what they say they will do. You can discuss what they say in their speeches—not their voice or the way they stand or some such, but the content of what they say. That is what you should be basing your decisions on, and that is what will keep you from stepping into the quicksand of lashon hora.

Thank you for bringing this to my attention. I think that I will be announcing an assembly to clarify this for all the students. "

After a few questions, Asher and Efraim left their rebbi's office with greater clarity and considerable relief.

"So, pretty much, we just vote for whoever says what we agree with in their speeches, right?" asked Asher. Efraim's attention was not on Asher.

"Well, as far as I'm concerned, I think Dovid has earned my vote right now," replied Efraim laughing. "Anyone who can turn a bunch of rumors around like that has my vote." He pointed to the new poster on the cafeteria wall:

> **Yep, I'm ADHD:**
> **I am**
> **A**mazingly **D**edicated, **H**onest and **D**aring!
> ***Vote Dovid***
> **for Student Council President!**

I Should Have Watched My Words

Two friends go on a shopping trip. What might have been a fun experience turns into a big mess. Let's see what happens and why.

"You're wearing that green outfit that I saw yesterday? It's fine!" I said into my phone. "You look good in that one."

"Are you sure?" Ruthie's bright voice faded a little as I thought for a moment. Being friends with Ruthie was difficult for me. While she always attracted attention with her beautiful, straight brown hair and sparkly blue eyes, somehow, she was always looking for reassurance. Like the time we all shared a ride to our friend's birthday party, and Ruthie made us late because she was busy redoing her ponytail to look just so. Even then, Ruthie spent the whole party asking me how her hair looked. Couldn't she just relax?

"You don't think it makes me look fat?" Ruthie asked as she opened the front door of her house. Today we were going shopping for clothing for her two-year-old nephew, and Ruthie wanted to look "perfect" for our spree.

"You are so skinny, I don't think that anything could make you look fat," Shira, her older sister called out from across the family room.

"C'mon, we're leaving. Don't you want to come, too?" Ruthie called to Shira.

Ruthie and Shira bundled up in their winter coats and gloves, and the three of us walked down the steps and headed toward Thirteenth Avenue. As we walked the six short blocks, Ruthie pointed to her brown, shearling coat and looked at her sister. "Shira, what do you think? Does this coat make me look too pale?"

Shira looked at me and then at her sister and shook her head back and forth. "Ruthie, you look terrific."

We went in and out of stores until we found what we were looking for at the Bambini Baby shop. Ruthie picked out some adorable striped blue and white cotton tops with matching blue corduroy pants, a green and yellow outfit and a packet of adorable socks. The store was packed and we waited about ten minutes until we got to the register. Just then, Ruthie held the green outfit out at arm's length. "I'm not sure I really like this outfit. What do you guys think?"

I glanced behind us and saw that there was a long line of customers waiting to check out.

"It's cute!" I said quickly.

"It's fine," Shira agreed.

"But look at the way these cuffs look, they're..." All I could focus on was the tapping foot of the woman behind me and the impatient glares from people behind *her*.

That's when I completely lost it. "Your nephew will LOVE the outfits. Just PAY for them!" I squeezed past her and went to stand a bit past the register. Shira came and joined me.

"Why is your sister so insecure?" I asked Shira. I was so furious at that moment that I didn't pay attention to how loudly I was speaking. I clenched my teeth and continued, "She is so high maintenance!"

At that moment, Ruthie finished paying for the items, grabbed the shopping bag, and ran past us, right out the door.

Shira and I were stunned. "Did she just run away?" asked Shira, quickly buttoning her coat and following. I did the same.

When we got outside, Ruthie was nowhere in sight.

"I can't believe it. Where did she go?" My voice cracked

"She's very sensitive these days." Shira cleared her throat. "I guess what you said really got to her."

I knew I should have watched my words. I had a nasty habit of letting my feelings slip right out. Like the time I was eating at Bubbie's house, and I told her in front of all of the cousins that the brisket was burnt and I was therefore allergic to it. The other kids laughed, but, of course, Daddy scolded me for that one. Bubbie, being the tolerant and loving person she is, thought it was entertaining so I got away with it. And that time my friend slept over? I told her that her breath stank when she woke up in the morning. She didn't seem offended at the time, so I figured it was okay. But, maybe it really wasn't okay; maybe I was too blunt.

All I knew was that today my words had caused my friend to run away. I looked at Shira as I pulled my gloves on. "Where do we even begin to look for her?"

"I know her favorite store is Mechayah Electronics. We should check in there," Shira said, pointing at the neon sign flashing down the block.

As we approached the store, Shira looked at me, biting her lip, "I really hope we find Ruthie; she's never done this before. I love my sister and don't want anything bad to happen to her." I felt a chill run through my body.

Mechayah was brightly lit, with everything from shavers to DVD players and cameras lined up on sparkling glass counters. The store was crowded for a Sunday morning, and every register had a long line of people waiting to pay for their purchases. Shira and I decided to stick together and walk down each aisle.

"I don't see her anywhere. This is crazy." My voice got louder as I felt my heart racing. What if we couldn't find Ruthie? What if something horrible happened to her, just because of me? I didn't want to tell Shira my thoughts. Instead I said, "We need to comb the area and go store to store." Shira thought a moment and said, "Hoenig's toy store on the corner of 48th, let's check there."

"Of course, great idea." I let out a brief sigh as I imagined finding Ruthie looking at toys in one of the aisles.

I ran toward the small toy store that was a favorite spot in Boro Park.

"Bet she's in the collector's doll section there," Shira said as we dashed toward the store. I was hoping to find her and have this episode over and done with. The thought that I kept pushing away slipped to the forefront. What if we couldn't find her? What if Ruthie wasn't at Hoenig's? What if something had happened to her? I pushed that line of thought away once more, while at the same time pushing open the large, front glass door of the shop. There was a long line of ladies with children in tow waiting to purchase their toys.

"Ru-uthie!" I called.

"Shh!" Shira said, poking me in the ribs with her arm. She jutted her chin in the direction of the people on line. They were staring. Oops.

"You start on that side and I'll start on this end and we'll meet in the middle," I told Shira pointing to the right and left walls of the store. We set off. I ran, looking up each and every aisle. Where was she?

A few minutes later, Shira met me in the baby toy section. Her eyes looked watery and her face was pale. "She's not here," she sighed dejectedly. "I don't know how we can...wait! I just remembered! We have emergency cellphones that my father makes us bring along when we are out. I totally forgot about it until now."

"That's great!" I said. "Let's call her!"

"She doesn't carry a purse. Did you see whether my sister put hers in a pocket when we left?"

I thought back to our leaving the house that morning. We had put on our coats, but I didn't recall Ruthie putting the cellphone in her pocket. I shrugged.

"I don't know, but it's worth a try. Let's call her!" I said. Shira opened her purse and took out her own cell. She turned it on and dialed the number, both of us waiting anxiously. I could hear Shira mumbling, "Please, please Hashem, let her be okay." I quickly added a prayer of my own.

"No answer. Maybe she went home. I'll try there," Shira said when the answering machine came on. "It's ringing."

I could faintly hear their mother's voice answer the phone.

"Have you seen Ruthie? She's where? She's in her room?"

I saw Shira's body relax as she said, "Everything's fine, Mom. We just stopped off at the electronics store, but we're coming right home."

Shira looked at me, shaking her head. "I should have tried that first. I'm so glad that Ruthie went home rather than wander around somewhere out here." I nodded with fervent agreement. Boy, was I relieved. I closed my eyes. *Thank you, Hashem, for keeping Ruthie safe.*

As we hurried to Shira and Ruthie's home, I began thinking about how I always felt that I could be blunt if there was a good enough reason for it. In any given situation, I would just speak my mind. After all, wasn't honesty the best policy?

But after today's incident, I realized that I really needed to watch my speech. Next time, I thought, I'll just bite my tongue and keep quiet. Maybe, if I wait until I'm calm, I can deal with a problem without saying something hurtful.

When we arrived at Shira's house, we went straight to Ruthie's room and knocked on the door. Ruthie was on the bed, tucking tissue paper into the boxes with the baby gifts. There were two rolls of wrapping paper lying next to her.

"You were mean to me," she said as I entered her room. "And I thought my own *sister* would stick up for me," she added as Shira followed me in.

"I'm so sorry Ruthie," I said. "I have a bad habit of being too blunt. I need to work on that. I really didn't mean to hurt you. I was just embarrassed for you, because all those women were waiting in line and your hesitating was making them wait even longer. I should have just drawn your attention to that and not lost my cool."

Shira apologized next and gave her sister a big hug. "You really didn't give me a chance to stick up for you, you know," Shira told her. "You ran out so fast, we couldn't even see your jet stream after you left." Ruthie smiled.

We told her about how we went from store to store looking for her.

She looked at the two of us and laughed. "I guess I gave you guys a real scare today. I'm sorry about that. Take off your coats, and make yourselves at home." She thought for another moment and said, "And I have to work on being less sensitive and particular..." Suddenly her eyes gleamed with mischief, "but I still can't figure out which wrapping paper to choose, what do you think?" she said holding up both rolls of paper.

There was a trio of laughter.

A Quiet Itch

Blimi really tries to watch her words. But things get tricky for her when a case of lice is found in her classroom. What happens next is amazing.

"There will be a lice check later today, before lunch," Ms. Wolff, our English teacher, informed us.

There was a hush, then a ripple of whispers. Nineteen girls can create a serious amount of rustling while taking out their notebooks and speculating on the why's of lice checking.

Lice! Images of tiny bugs, hundreds of them, crawling all over my scalp, popped into my head. My head began to itch as I noticed a few other girls around me scratching their heads.

Next period we had a science unit and I was paired up with Chumi.

"Do you know who has lice?" she asked me.

"I don't want to know," I said, interrupting her before she could blurt out the girl's name.

Just this morning at breakfast, my mother and I had been talking about school.

"I know lice are going around," she had said, scrunching up her nose. Mom couldn't stand being around most bugs, and lice were the worst. "But I don't want to know who has it unless there is something specific I can do to help that person." Mom looked at me meaningfully. "It's pure lashon hora, so try to avoid any discussions about who might or might not have lice, okay?"

"I won't tell you, and I won't talk to the girls in school about it either," I said with a smile. I was good at keeping my word, but sometimes keeping from listening to things in school was a big challenge.

"Why can't you tell us who has lice so we can be careful?" my little brother blurted out from behind his yogurt. He was always very practical.

"Because, think about it...." I stopped to give him a chance to do so. "Nobody would want to sit next to, play with, or even be near someone who has lice."

"Guess not," Shlomo answered, "but if you have lice, don't you have to stay home until it's all gone? Like chicken pox? Then you go back to school and you're not contagious anymore. So what's the big deal?" and then, having solved the problem to his satisfaction, he changed the topic to baseball, his current favorite topic of conversation.

I knew though, that with lice it wasn't that simple. With lice, you weren't sick. No one felt sorry for you. You had *bugs* in your hair—creepy, crawly things that could jump from someone else's hair to yours. Even though it didn't really make sense, having lice was a stigma. Kids felt that it was something someone got because they weren't clean enough, or careful enough. We learned that this wasn't true, at least not in our country, but still, it *felt* to most kids like it was the sort of thing you got because you weren't doing something right. It was a mark, a stain, a taint.

After lunch, during Ivrit, our Hebrew language class, I noticed that one girl was absent. Chava's desk was empty. Her usual, cheerfully haphazard pile of papers was missing.

"Wonder if she has lice?" some of the girls whispered at recess.

I didn't talk about it, and tried not to listen. I took my Rainbow Loom and went to sit with another girl, and together we made bracelets. A few days passed by, and Chava remained absent. When she finally returned on Thursday, two other girls were absent.

At recess, many of the girls stayed a bit distant from Chava. I figured that some of them thought that she had been home with a case of lice. No one really spoke about it, but I saw that girls were hesitant to play with her.

"Want to make a bracelet?" I offered.

"Sure!" Chava smiled and a sat down next to me, and we each wove our own fishtail bracelet.

I felt a great big burst like a happy tickle in my stomach that day, knowing that I had been extra kind to Chava and that I had ignored that sneaky feeling inside to also stay away from her.

The trouble began soon after.

"Lice check after lunch tomorrow," our teacher called out. "Take out your Halacha notebooks."

Our lice checks had become so routine that it was almost like brushing our teeth before bed. Lice check, girl absent the next day. Girls talk about her. Girl returns to school, is shunned for a while. I stay friendly.

After lunch the next day we lined up, waiting to have our hair combed and checked in the back of our classroom.

Mrs. Kramer, one of the volunteer mothers for lice checking, inspected my hair. She combed and combed and combed again. She asked me to tilt my head more to the right, and I felt her poking behind my ear and at the base of my neck. What was she doing? What was taking her so long? I wasn't too worried, because just two days ago someone had checked me and said I was fine. But, unexpectedly, Mrs. Kramer whispered in my ear, "Blimi, I found one nit. Go to the...never mind, sit down, continue your math class, and I'll take care of it."

My mind went blank. A nit? That's impossible! I used special shampoo every single night. And I wasn't even itchy, not even a tiny bit.

Just a few weeks before, I had bought some pretty glitter, and had thrown a handful up into the air, getting a good amount into my hair. Sparkly magic dust, I had called it. I thought it was cool. Maybe that's what she had found in my hair?

I looked at my math sheet, but I couldn't concentrate. Then the room intercom came on: "Mrs. Green, please send Blimi down to the office."

When I got to the office, one of the lice checkers tried to look through my hair, but by then it was too tangled to do a thorough job. I kept wincing and calling out, "ow!" when she tried pulling the hairs apart.

"We'll call your mother. She needs to wash and comb your hair so that we can check you properly tomorrow."

The next day was a busy one, and it wasn't until the last period that Mrs. Kramer checked me again. She combed and combed and checked behind my left ear. "You need to go to the office," she said, her sweet voice sounding like a caring mother.

It was there that the school nurse, who had the most experience, checked me and pulled something from my hair. What was it?

Glitter? Or, maybe a sesame seed from my roll at lunch?

"Nits are small eggs that stick to the hair. They are whitish, with a little bit of brown at the tip," my friend's mother had told me.

I thought to myself, *I know they're making a terrible mistake!*

Either way, school let out just in time, and as my carpool dropped me off, I arrived home with tears in my eyes.

"I heard the news," Mom said as I came into the house.

"Don't make a big deal over it," I said.

My brother, Shlomo, rushed in from school and must have overheard part of the conversation. "Blimi has li-ice, Blimi has li-ice," he blurted out.

"Stop!" Mom used her firm voice. "We don't make fun of each other and we don't make people feel bad. We don't know if Blimi has lice. We'll see. But if she does, we need to take care of it. That's what families do. They take care of each other, not hurt each other's feelings. Now, what do you have to say?"

"I'm sorry, Blimi," Yaakov looked truly contrite, "I hope you don't have lice. I hope you get all better." Mom smiled and gave him a hug.

"That's much better. Now, sit down and eat the snack I have on the table for you, and then go out and play. I'm sure Aaron will be outside soon. Invite him to play with you in the backyard while I help Blimi wash her hair and check it carefully." She turned to me, "young lady, we have a date at our very own spa with a warm, lovely shower and a special comb guaranteed to make your hair clean, soft and shiny. Come, let us proceed." Mom always knew how to turn an awkward, sometimes unpleasant situation into something warm and special. Hand in hand we went upstairs. I no longer felt so frightened and upset.

Hair freshly washed, I sat while Mom sectioned off parts of my hair, carefully running the comb through each strand.

"Nothing here" she said, pulling my hair to the side, "and here, and here and here. Just lots of beautiful, shiny hair. I guess it's been a while since I've spent so long on your hair. You're such a capable young lady now that you mostly take care of it by yourself. I miss combing through all these lovely honey colored locks." Mom combed and checked, combed and checked. So gently did her fingers move through my hair and over my head and with such loving words that the knot in my heart slowly loosened. Instead of a dreaded experience, it was actually very calming and relaxing. I trusted my mother.

"I don't see a thing," she said with a smile. "I'm going to call my friend Chaya for double verification, to be absolutely sure, but I don't think she will find anything.

When Chaya came over to check me, she brought a different comb that she had used when her children were in Israel. Apparently, they had contracted a bad case of lice there a few years back.

"Nothing at all in here," Chaya said happily after a few minutes of checking. Shower one more time and change your sheets and pillow cases just to cover all the bases, but I don't see anything at all."

"I am so relieved," I said.

"It is wonderful to know you don't have lice," Mom said. "But, just so you know, if we did find a few nits, we would have just removed them and you would have been just as fine and good to go. If we had found any live bugs, well, you know how difficult that would have been for me." She shuddered dramatically. "But I would have knuckled down and got rid of them as well."

"Thanks, Mom, you're the best!" I hugged her hard.

The next day, I returned to school where the school nurse checked me over once again. I was glad that no one from my class was in the office. While I could feel comfortable just dealing naturally with lice with my Mom, getting stared at and shunned by the girls was another matter. It was so hard to take.

"You can go back to class," the nurse said with a cheerful wave of her hand. "Nit free."

And as I walked back to class with a skip in my step, I remembered how I was careful about my speech. We had learned once in class that the reward for not speaking lashon hora was a great one. By not speaking lashon hora against others in the class who might have had lice, I didn't embarrass anyone. Maybe, just maybe, Hashem had protected me from other's suspicious looks and embarrassment.

It would have been difficult having to be out from school for days, having to have my hair checked over and over again or possibly even cut. It would have been hard to deal with washing all my clothes, my bedding and rugs and stuffed animal collection. But most of all, it would have been hard knowing that others might be speaking lashon hora about me. I'm not sure why, but the whispers and stares of other girls can be harder to take than just about anything. I ran to my seat, and sat down quietly before anyone could even guess that I might have been out. And I said a quiet thank you to Hashem.

Fun & Facts

Shmiras Halashon - שמירת הלשון

Guarding One's Speech

Why is guarding our speech so important? Aren't words basically harmless?

Think about a time when someone said something mean or thoughtless to you or about you. It *hurt.* It hurts our feelings, and it hurts others' opinions of us. It also hurts the person speaking those words, because it strengthens insensitivity and lack of care for others.

The Torah tells us: *Lo seilech rachil b'amecha*—do not go around spreading gossip or saying bad things about someone—even if what you are saying is true. Doing so falls under the category of לשון הרע—evil speech, or gossip.
(Leviticus 19:16)

Just Say No to Lashon Horah

Cool Fact:

Have you ever heard someone say, "Bite your tongue"? This is an expression that means to keep quiet; keep your thoughts to yourself—particularly harmful or negative thoughts. It might sound silly, but it is a real idea to control how we speak, because if you *did* clamp your teeth on your tongue, you wouldn't be able to speak at all. So, when you are tempted to speak lashon horah, just stop yourself from speaking anything at all, until you can say something good. Be strong inside and just say, "No!"

Neat Trick:

Next time you are tempted to speak lashon hora, run to the water fountain or take a quick sip from a water bottle, and hold the water in your mouth for thirty seconds. Notice how it is not possible to talk. That's an easy way to put a gap between the temptation and the thought to NOT speak lashon hora.

True Story: Ta'anis Dibur

Meet Leora G. who, once per year, does not speak for 25 hours. What is she doing and why does she do it?

Leora G. is a special woman who lives in Yerushalayim. Every Yom Kippur she goes on a twenty-five-hour speech fast. A ta'anis dibur. For that entire period, she refrains from speaking to all people, only using her speech to daven and make brachos.[1] She learned to do this many years ago from a friend of hers whom she met in seminary.

Leora says, "I always felt that lashon hora was one of the biggest things I needed to work on, since I like to schmooze." She felt that Yom Kippur was the perfect time for her to step back, completely refrain from any lashon hora, and just think

1 Please note that when deciding to take upon yourself a fast or any practice that is extra, something that is not part of what halacha tells us to do, we should ask our rabbi if it is both permitted and acceptable.

and connect to Hashem. By keeping from speaking at all, she was able to accomplish this.

For Leora, taking a break from speaking is not too difficult. "On Yom Kippur we are mostly in shul, spending the day davening and not dealing with eating, so not speaking isn't too hard for me," she said. Things did get a bit tough for Leora once she got married and had children. For a while then, Leora took a break from her ta'anis dibur

"But once the kids got older, I again took on this custom," she said. "It's funny to see my younger kids roll their eyes and think it a bit crazy when I'm not talking at all on Yom Kippur."

How is Leora able keep her ta'anis dibur? She explains, "I am very blessed to have a daughter who helps me with my ta'anis dibur. She can almost read my mind, so that whenever I need something, I don't have to talk, and she is able to help me."

One can imagine all sorts of amusing scenarios when picturing a mother not talking for an entire day. Imagine her trying to tell an older child how to find a younger sibling's stuffed rabbit. With hand motions and acting, (picture her holding hands up beside her ears like bunny ears and hop hop hopping around) she would indicate how to go upstairs into the second room on the right, open the closet door and pull out the drawer one up from the bottom, then look all the way in the back. What a master at charades she might have to become. But through it all, she will not have uttered one single word of lashon hora.

When asked if she could share a story that occurred during her ta'anis dibur, Leora told us about the time when her family stayed in the Old City of Yerushalayim. "I ran into friends whom I haven't seen in years. They came up to me and wanted to talk." You can imagine the confusion these people felt when, instead of responding to their greetings, she remained quiet and motioned to her daughter. "Luckily," she laughed, "my daughter was able to explain to them that I wasn't talking for the entire day. I'm blessed to have my special ta'anis helper!"

Leora revealed what she gained from keeping this practice: "When I come out of my ta'anis dibur, I am much more careful with my speech. I realize that so much of what comes out of my mouth really isn't necessary. It's a great way for me to improve my middos."

(Personal communication, Leora G. Jerusalem, Israel, May 21, 2015)

We may not be able to keep a ta'anis dibur for an entire day, but perhaps we can set aside ten minutes, fifteen minutes, or even an hour each day in which we are particularly careful not to speak any lashon hora. If we stop ourselves from speaking about others in any form, for at least that time period, we will develop the mindfulness to be aware of our speech and find it getting easier to keep from speaking lashon hora the rest of the day.

Did You Know?

Our mesorah teaches us that people are not allowed to speak lashon hora even about themselves. So be careful, even when you are talking with your friends. Do not make fun of yourself or put yourself down (I'm so stupid, I can't do anything right, etc.). By putting yourself down, you are telling yourself and others that this wonderful person that Hashem made is somehow defective. Would Hashem make you less than you should be? And if you are not living up to what you think you should be doing, then you need to focus on figuring out how to get there, not putting yourself down for not being there already. We are here to *work* at growing, not *be* grown.

Talking is like email:

When you speak, imagine that your words are like an email or text that you just typed, but did not send. Once you make sure there are no wrong or damaging words in your email, only then is it ok to click SEND. The same is true with speaking. After your words come out of your mouth, it is impossible to take them back. So, the next time you are about to share some really juicy lashon hora or say something nasty, think twice before you speak—and don't press the SEND button.

I Smell Fire Game: (for two or more players)

Lashon hora is like a dangerous fire, which needs to be put out right away. In this game, each player takes a turn and thinks of a new way to put out the fire and stop someone from speaking lashon hora.

For example, the first player says, "When someone begins to speak lashon hora, I yell out, 'fire' and I change the topic."

Now it's the second player's turn.

That person says, "When someone begins to speak lashon hora, I yell out 'fire' and I put my hands over my ears. Each player has to suggest a new way to stop someone from speaking lashon hora, so they can put out the fire. Each player must say something different. If anyone repeats an idea, the game ends. A second way to play the game: Divide up into two teams. Each team has five minutes to write down a list of ways to put out the lashon hora fire. The team with the biggest list wins.

While these games give you ideas to think about, also realize that you should not embarrass someone by telling them that what they are saying is lashon hora. We must do it in an indirect and sensitive way. If you and your friends are working on not speaking lashon hora together, you can come up with a method that you all agree to, so that no one is offended.

Question:

Why do people speak lashon hora? Perhaps they want to lift themselves up by putting others down. They could be jealous of someone's accomplishment and think that by telling people something bad about him or her people will no longer feel good about that person. Sometimes we feel we will gain more friends if we have juicy things to relate about other people because our yetzer hora likes listening to negative talk and "do you know what so and so did?" *does* draw people to listen. But think, are those people really becoming your friends, or are they just looking to hear lashon hora?

What other reasons for people speaking lashon hora can you think of?

Did you know that speaking lashon hora could be the same as bullying?

Many times, bullies hurt people by picking a target and calling that person derogatory names. They might call a short person "Shrimpy" or an overweight person "Blubber." Then they get their followers to do the same. A bully will also often tell people nasty things about a person. Sometimes bullies will take something that is true and twist it into something bad, such as a classmate who has always done well on tests being jeered at for getting those marks because he or she is a cheater, or calling him or her a nerd or geek. Bullies might also just imply something without actually saying what that something is. For instance, if one student turns to his or her friends and says, "You don't want to talk to *him/her,"* implying he/she's not like us or is somehow defective—that, too, is bullying, and ALL of these are forms of lashon hora.

Every one of these forms of lashon hora is extremely harmful to both the speaker and the one the horrible speech is directed toward. People being bullied are often too weak, timid, scared or shy to stand up for themselves. It is up to you, to every person who sees bullying, to step up and stand up for the one being bullied. Telling the bully it is lashon hora will not usually work, since the bully is most commonly not open to listening. Stand by the one being bullied and tell the bully to stop. Unless there is real physical danger, take a stand. The more kids who do this, the less power that bully has. If you think the bully is dangerous or too hard to handle, go tell a teacher or parent.

DO NOT LET IT GO. KEEPING QUIET IS NOT AN OPTION. The one being bullied may feel that pain for the rest of their lives.

We are responsible for one another.
Take action and stand up for someone who needs you.

Chapter Six

Nothing but the Truth

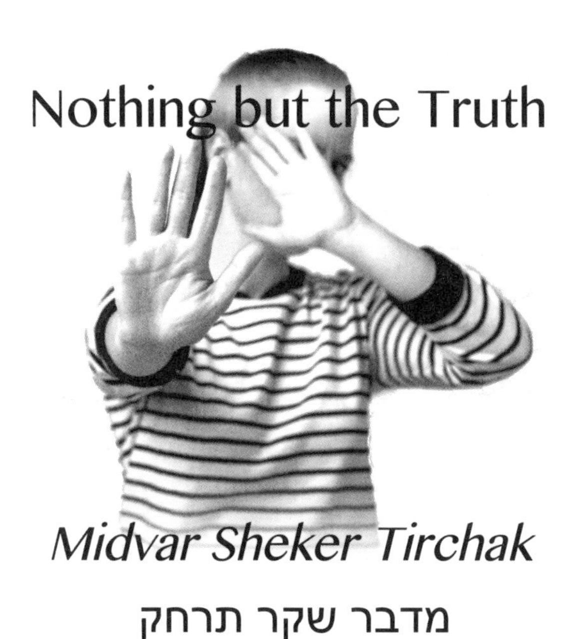

Midvar Sheker Tirchak

מדבר שקר תרחק

Stay Far Away from Falsehood (Lying)

A Price to Pay

Meira's father saved up to buy his wife a special gift for their thirtieth wedding anniversary. When Meira can't resist handling the delicate crystals, she gets into a world of trouble.

Dad knew that Mom loved beautiful things. She was always making our home cozier and more beautiful by adding pretty pillows to our sofa, sewing filmy curtains with embroidered leaves for the windows or painting pretty pottery. She often found special deals in stores for some pretty item or other to add to our home. Dad noticed that she had a particular interest in the sparkly chandeliers some of her friends had. She would often stare at them and remark on how beautiful they were. So, for their thirtieth wedding anniversary, Dad special ordered a handmade chandelier from a glassblower in Murano, Italy.

You should have seen the excitement and love in Mom's eyes when she opened the box and saw what was inside. And when Dad told her that this one-of-a-kind lamp took half a year to create, she could hardly wait to hang it up. Dad had already arranged for the electrician to come on Tuesday. Mom carefully rewrapped the pieces, leaving just a few out on the table on their plastic bubble wrap so that she could gaze at them from time to time.

"Do not touch any of them," Dad warned my brother and me. "The crystal is really fragile and we don't want to take a chance on any accidents happening. Right?" He gave us his "I'm really serious" look. I stared at the parts of the chandelier that Mom had carefully laid out on the table. There were six crystals attached by delicate chains, sparkling like diamonds in the light cast by our ceiling lights. I just knew they would sparkle even more when the morning light streamed in through our dining room window.

I don't know what got into me, but the next morning I woke up early, and, while Mom and Dad still slept, I crept quietly downstairs to our dining room. My hands were itching to touch that fine Italian glass. I knew myself to be a really careful person and didn't worry about dropping things. I hadn't dropped something breakable since I was a little kid. I reached out to one of the chains and slowly lifted it by the tiny top hook that would attach it to the chandelier. Up came three of the oval crystals, each connected by a delicate chain, the middle one longer than the others like a triangle of raindrops. Light sparkled almost blindingly from each of the crystals, reflecting in wonderful, glittering patterns over the table, ceiling and walls. I stared and stared, trying to take in this whole beautiful room of twinkling lights. *"No wonder Mom was so happy to receive this gift,"* I thought, *"she always found ways to make our home more beautiful, and this was the most wondrous thing yet!"* I looked down at the crystals and took one into my palm. It felt as smooth as silk and was as light as a bird's egg. Totally entranced, I once again started lifting the trio of crystals high into the air to catch the most sunlight when a sudden noise caused me to flinch. Crash! All three crystals hit the ceramic floor and shattered into a million tiny shards. I stood there in shock, my mouth opened wide. *What*? I felt like I couldn't breathe, my heart thumping wildly in my chest. *Mom's new chandelier! I've ruined it! She'll be so upset! My dad will be so disappointed in me. Everyone will blame me. I thought I was being so careful. How did this happen? What should I do?* My thoughts flashed like lightning. *I've got to clean this mess up quickly before anyone sees!*

I ran to the broom closet and grabbed the broom and dustpan. I noticed that my palms were sweaty. *What had I done? Had my parents heard anything?* I heard a rustling and then the kitchen side door opened. I bit my lip and turned around quickly to see who was there.

It was only Maria, our Spanish helper. "*Hola!*" she called cheerily as she entered the kitchen from the back porch. She noticed the glass mess I was sweeping up and asked me, "*Necessita ayuda*?" which means, "Do you need help?"

Maria had recently move to the United States from Guatemala and understood simple sentences in English, but had a harder time speaking the language. Because I had taken two and a half years of Spanish in school, I was able to speak to her a bit in Spanish, and, more importantly, was often able to translate simple sentences for my parents.

"*Gracias!*" I thanked Maria as she whisked the broom across the floor, sweeping up the glass and emptying the dustpan into the kitchen trashcan.

I heard footsteps on the stairs and held my breath as my parents came down and entered the dining room. *Oh no!* I thought. They still hadn't noticed anything was wrong. I slipped into the kitchen where I could hide, but see everything.

"I want to hang it right over the table," Mom said to Dad and pointed to a spot on the ceiling.

"Fine." Dad said. "I don't quite remember how big the whole thing is. We'll have to check." He bent down and gently lifted the main part of the chandelier out of the box and then carefully unwrapped the bubble wrap. Next, he gently pulled out the glass crystals and chains in their bubble wrap, setting each one down separately near the lamp.

"Hey, aren't there supposed to be six crystal sets here?" My heart seemed to thump in my chest. Dad had realized that there were only five. He counted them again and rechecked the box.

"What's that?" Mom walked in closer to the lamp. "One set is missing?"

My parents began looking around to see if any of the crystals were on the chairs or floor when they noticed Maria at the other end of the room, busily sweeping vigorously at the last tiny pieces of glass. Mom looked at Dad.

"George, I see small bits of glass in the pile Maria is sweeping. Could that be...?"

She couldn't even voice the possibility. I wanted to run a million miles away ... to be anywhere but there.

"Maria, did you do this?" Mom pointed at the glass on the floor. "Did you break one of the crystals from the lamp?" she asked pointing to the other crystals laid out on the table.

"Si, I clean up," she answered, a confused look on her face.

"Meira?" called my mom. *How did she know I was in the kitchen? Did she know I was the one who broke the crystals?* I walked hesitantly into the dining room.

"Yes?" I squeaked.

"Could you please ask Maria if she did this?" Mom asked pointing to the glass shards in the wastebasket. I bit my lip and tried to get myself to admit it was my fault, but just couldn't do it. I felt so guilty. At the same time, I didn't want my mother to be upset with me, didn't want to be the cause of her sadness and definitely didn't want to face my dad's disappointment, especially since he had worked so hard to get this for my mom.

I turned to Maria and asked, "Tu hace eso?" (Did you do this?) Of course, she thought we were asking if she had swept the glass up, not whether or not she was the one who broke it. She didn't understand what the fuss was about.

"Si, I do, yo limpiar bueno," she responded, nodding her head. "Me asegure de que no habia mas vidrio en el suelo. All clean." She was telling us that she cleaned the floor well, making sure there was no more glass on the floor.

Mom looked like she couldn't decide whether to yell or cry. Dad looked angry. I felt relieved. *Wow, a way out of my problem. I'll let Maria take the blame for breaking the chandelier.*

So, I said, "Maria didn't mean to break it, Mom and Dad, she said she's sorry." *Maybe this plan would work.* I thought that the sick feeling in my stomach was because I was worried about being found out.

"Maria, we are very upset! You had no business touching the chandelier," my Mother said with a sob in her voice. Maria looked at me. She was confused. Father put his arm around my mother's shoulders and said, "Let's go into the living room and talk about what we should do." He led her away, and Maria was left staring at me.

"Cual es el problema? (What is the problem?)" She asked me. "You mama okay?"

"Esta bien," (It's okay) I answered her, giving her a pat on the arm. "You did a good job of cleaning." I didn't know how to say the lamp broke and my mother was upset. Plus, I had just blamed it on Maria, and I couldn't tell her *that.* I followed my parents to the living room and paused in the entryway. I heard my mother wondering if they could take the cost of replacing the broken pieces out of Maria's pay.

I chewed my lip with worry. I didn't feel right not telling the truth. What if Maria got fired just because of me? I thought about her two small children. I imagined them crying because their mother was out of a job and they had no money. But I couldn't just tell them what happened. I had already said it was Maria who did it.

"Things happen for a reason," my father was reassuring my Mom. "We'll find out how much it costs to order replacement parts and trust that things will work out according to Hashem's plan. Maybe there's a reason we have to wait a bit to put up your beautiful lamp, but we'll get it done. Don't you worry," he added softly. I couldn't hear what else he told her as I turned and ran upstairs to get ready for school.

That whole day in school I couldn't concentrate. I sat in Chumash class and fiddled with my pencil, unable to take proper notes. We were learning about Adam and Chava and the snake. Each of them was punished for not listening to Hashem's command, but both Adam and Chava tried to tell

Hashem that it was someone else's fault that they did what they did. Perhaps, if they had admitted their error and said they were sorry, they might have been given a lesser punishment.

It wasn't *exactly* the same, but I had convinced my parents that Maria had been the one to break the crystals. I shifted blame to try and save myself embarrassment and facing the consequences of what I did.

I knew what I had to do. I couldn't stand that horrible feeling inside any longer.

As soon as my father got home that night, I rushed into the kitchen where both my parents were. "*I* broke the chandelier, not Maria. I did it!" Tears ran down my cheeks, and I threw my arms around my mother. "I'm sorry Mom. I know how much it meant to you."

"You did?" Mom said. Then, there was a pause. "Why would you touch my chandelier after Dad told you not to?"

"Why did you lie to us?" Dad asked. "You almost got Maria fired!"

My parents were shooting questions left and right. I answered in a low tone. "The chandelier was so beautiful, Mom, I just wanted to touch it. You know I'm careful with delicate things. I always wash and dry the crystal wine glasses Dad uses and I've never broken any of them. I thought I could handle the crystals as well." For a moment I forgot myself and continued, "You should have seen how gorgeous the room was when the sunlight went through those crystals! The whole room became a magical place of sparkling lights reflecting everywhere!" My parents were staring at me and did not look very pleased.

"Um, well, what I mean is, I picked up one of the chains with the three attached crystals and was looking at all the reflections when Maria made a sound at the door and I jumped. And, well, the chain slipped from my fingers and...and..." I covered my face with my hands and sobbed. "I'm so sorry! I didn't mean to break them and they were so beautiful!"

"And you blamed Maria," Dad said. I looked at him through my tears and took a deep, steadying breath.

"I shouldn't have blamed her. It was a terrible thing to do. When you came down the stairs, I was afraid of disappointing you and of being punished. I felt terrible about it all day, and I know that lying was worse than just telling the truth, and I'll give you my baby sitting money until the crystals are paid for!" I said all in a rush.

Mom and Dad both sighed. I saw that Mom was looking at me with love, rather than disgust.

"Hashem expects us to be honest, no matter how badly we feel," Dad said. "We have to be strong to take responsibility for our actions."

"I realize that, and I made a big mistake." Mom shook her head and took my hand.

"What do you realize?" she asked.

"That even though I was scared to tell you, I feel better inside telling the truth. And I really feel bad that I blamed Maria and that *she* would have been the one to get punished for something she didn't do. And she probably wouldn't have understood why, because she didn't do anything wrong."

Mom nodded and my Dad said, "What you did was wrong, and you realize that. You offer your baby-sitting money to pay back the cost, but that will not be enough. We can sit down together and work out a schedule of payment when you work this summer, until you pay us back." I nodded. I had already planned to work in the summer, and I thought Dad was being more than fair.

"But there is one other thing that you didn't address," he continued.

I looked at my Dad questioningly.

"Think about it. There is one other part of this that is very important. It is the very first thing you did wrong." I thought for a minute, and then I knew.

"You told me not to touch Mom's gift, and I did it anyway." I looked down at my feet. "I'm sorry Dad. I should have listened to you. None of this would have happened if I had."

Dad nodded and put his hand under my chin, raising it so that I looked into his eyes. "Meirale, there is nothing that is as important as being honest with each other. When we admit a wrong, we are trusting someone else with our failing, and that is *very hard.* But it also makes you stronger, and us a stronger family. We can work out what to do together."

I looked at Mom. "You aren't sad that you have to wait for new crystals to be made and sent? That I ruined your beautiful surprise?"

My mother put her arm around my shoulder. "You matter more to me than any *thing,* Meira, and the beauty of your growing into a responsible young lady is more wonderful than any other gift I can be given. I might be a *little* sad, but I can wait for more crystals to be sent. I would have been *very* sad if you weren't honest with us. But you were and we are very proud of you." I looked at Dad, and he nodded with a smile. Boy, was telling the truth hard. But it sure was worth it.

Honest Change

Yossi can't afford a ticket to the Boys' Choir Concert. Is it a miracle when money suddenly comes his way?

I really, really wanted to see the Boys' Choir Spectacular concert. It was the final show of their tour, and they were coming to my city to perform for Chol HaMoed Sukkos. It was now a few days before Rosh Hashanah, and I couldn't wait.

My friend, Mordechai, had amazing tickets to the show that he had purchased through a one-day, early bird special. The tickets were for seats in the center row and close to the front—the best seats ever! Those were exactly the tickets I wanted. When he found out that some of his other friends were going all-night laser tagging the night of the concert, Mordechai, or Mordy as he preferred to be called, wasn't so keen about going to the show. His parents told him that it was okay if he sold the tickets and used the money for laser tagging. Mordy told me he'd sell me his three tickets for twenty-five dollars each, which was an amazing deal as those seats were now selling for $75 apiece. The problem was, I didn't have seventy-five dollars to pay for them. I had used up the last of my saved spending money on an end of summer three-day trip to New York with our rebbi.

Mordy didn't want to take a chance on selling the tickets separately as he needed almost that much to pay for his laser tag night. I asked around, but none of my friends were interested in buying a ticket. Some had already purchased their tickets, some didn't want to go, and a few had parents who would be taking them and paying for them. Mordy wanted an answer by the end of the week; otherwise, he had a cousin who would buy the tickets the next Sunday.

I sat down and brainstormed, trying to think of ways to earn some quick money. I could offer to babysit my nephew. Nah. He was way too overactive. I could offer to mow a few lawns. But that would mean mowing at least six lawns, and there just wasn't enough time to do that.

I decided to plead with my parents.

"Mom and Dad, I really, really, want to go to the Chol HaMoed concert! Mordy will give me his three tickets for $75. That's a *huge* deal! Those tickets sell for $75 each! *Please* can we buy them? Then we can all go together! And before you ask, Mordy won't sell me just one. Only all three together."

"Sorry, Yossi. Tickets to your last concert cost us over a hundred dollars because you 'really, really didn't want to miss it.' We know how much you love your music, so we put aside the money for that. But one concert a year is all we budgeted for. You'll have to find a way to come up with the money for this on your own." Dad looked at me over his cup of coffee, his eyes twinkling with humor. "I know how enterprising you can be when you want something. I'll be interested to see what you come up with."

"But, Asher's cousin from Florida sings in the choir. The three of us really got to know each other last summer. It's almost like family!"

My dad shook his head without saying a word. My mom's eyebrows went up—which meant she wasn't buying my reasoning at all. "All the more incentive for you to earn the money," she said.

I sighed and nodded agreement. I didn't think to explain that I needed the money by the end of the week. For some reason, at that moment I just felt that it wouldn't help, since my parents were both convinced it was my job to come up with the money myself.

I couldn't think of a way to do it. I was desperate. So, as I always did when I didn't know what to do, I davened.

"Hashem, maybe I'm asking a little too much, but I really want to see the Boys Choir concert this year. Their music is so special. Listening to it makes me feel closer to You. So, is there any way You can help me get money to pay for the ticket? Please?"

Two days passed. Then—it happened. I thought it was a miracle. I had ridden my bike over to Kosher Mart to pick up some pasta, veggies and sauce for Mom—she was making my favorite dinner. The food cost $9.75. I handed the cashier a fifty-dollar bill, and she gave me change, which I stuffed into my pocket. Mom had told me to get home fast, so I didn't count the change.

"Thanks for coming home right away." Mom took the bag of groceries from me and went into the kitchen to unpack. I pulled the change out of my pocket and put it down on the kitchen table. I counted two dimes and a nickel, then the bills: five ones, one five, one ten, and one twenty. Wait. What was this? Stuck to the back of one of the twenties was the fifty-dollar bill I had given the cashier. I saw that a bit of leftover candy from my pocket had gotten on the bill and now it was stuck to one of the twenties. I carefully peeled the bills apart and stared. Now I had the change of $40.25 as well as a $50. Wow! The checkout lady had handed me $90.25. Was this Hashem's way of answering my prayer? I felt really strange about it and decided to keep it a secret. I left Mom's change on the table and slipped the extra fifty into my pocket. With the last twenty-five dollars I still had left from the summer, I now had enough money for the concert!

The next day was the last day before our break. I gave Mordy the money and he gave me the tickets.

I held the tickets and stared at them with wonder. It felt so good to have them without worrying about how to come up with the money. Yet, something was bothering me. Was this really a neis? A miracle that Hashem made happen in answer to my prayer? I knew I hadn't done anything to earn the money or even done something to deserve a miracle like that. But, maybe Hashem felt I should have it? I mean, it was *exactly* the amount I needed.

When I got home from school, Dad was fixing our lawnmower outside, while Mom was peeling potatoes at the kitchen sink. I wanted to tell them that I had bought the tickets, but I was nervous that they'd want to know where the money came from. And something was bothering me about how I got it, even if I didn't do anything wrong. At least, I didn't think so. Did I? I just wasn't sure.

So, I called my friend, Binny. He's one of those kids that can usually see through a muddle and evaluate a problem clearly. He's also a real learner and knows lots of halacha. I figured I'd ask his opinion.

"I've got a dilemma," I told him, "I'm hoping you can help me think this through."

"I'll try," Binny answered, "let me put my dilemma solving cap on," he quipped.

"You know the Boys Choir concert for Chol HaMoed Succos?" I asked.

"Yep, wish I could go but the tickets are a fortune," he told me.

"Well, you know how much I love singing. Especially *their* music. I really wanted to go to this, but I only had twenty-five bucks left over from the summer to pay for it."

"What are you getting at? You know I can't lend you money, Yos," I could hear noise in the background, "I have to go in a sec', dinner's ready."

"I'll be quick. I'm not asking you for money. The thing is, my parents told me I'd have to come up with the money if I want to go and Mordy had three tickets he was willing to sell as a group for only $75."

"Wow! What a deal! But, you said you only have twenty-five. You want me to buy one of them? I don't think I can right now."

"No, no. Just listen. I sort of davened for a miracle to happen, and...well... I *think* I got one?"

"What? You won the lottery?" Rafi joked.

"Funny. What happened was, I asked Hashem to help me and two days later, when I went to Kosher Mart, the checkout lady gave me fifty dollars too much. I think I got some Mike 'n Ike on the fifty my mom gave me and it got stuck to the change from the cashier."

"And you kept the money?"

"Why not?" I pretended like it was no big deal, but my heart was pounding. There was silence for a moment, then Rafi spoke very carefully.

"What did you do with the money?"

"I gave it to Mordy with my other $25 for the tickets he had," I told him.

"That's stealing, Yossi!" Rafi practically squeaked.

"But Hashem made it happen. Didn't He? I mean, the cashier gave me the *exact* amount I needed!"

"Listen, I have to go, Yossi, but maybe Hashem *did* answer you. But not like you think. Maybe He heard your tefillah and is showing you what is important. Maybe this is a test. You know? Like Avraham had ten tests? Maybe this is one of yours. Just maybe Hashem is giving you the chance to be stronger than your yetzer hora and do what is right, not what you *want.* Yom Kippur is coming, and if I were you, I wouldn't want to have stealing on my conscience."

I felt as if all the air had been sucked out of my lungs. I could barely draw a breath.

Stealing, stealing...the words kept echoing in my head. This was stealing? *Was* this a test?

Maybe Rafi was wrong. I hadn't taken the money deliberately, so why was it stealing? I didn't want to think about not going to the concert. About giving the tickets back to Mordy. And how would he pay for his laser tag? Didn't this all work out perfectly for everyone?

Slowly, I went to my room to think. Eventually I faced what I hadn't wanted to look at before. The store didn't get what it should have. They were out fifty dollars. So that meant....I closed my eyes and swallowed hard. That meant it *was* stealing, because I had kept something that didn't belong to me.

I blinked a few tears away and took a deep breath. I needed to do the right thing.

I ran downstairs and found my parents. My father had finished fixing the lawn mower, and they were both sitting in the family room while dinner cooked.

"I have to tell you something," I began. My parents looked at me and waited.

"You know how you asked me to pay for my own ticket to the concert?" Dad nodded. "Well, when Mom asked me to pick up some food at Kosher Mart, the clerk gave me too much change by accident. I used it—plus $25 that I had in savings—to buy those super tickets from Mordy."

My dad started to say something, but my mom put her hand on his arm and the two exchanged one of those looks they have where they understand each other.

"Go on," Mom said, "What else do you have to say?"

"I realize that I was wrong. I made a big mistake." I told them and looked down at my feet. "I asked Hashem to help me and I thought that getting that fifty was His answer. But now I think it was just a test. I know it was wrong to keep it. But, I'm not sure what to do now to make it right. I don't think Mordy will take the tickets back and give me the fifty because he needed the money to buy a ticket for laser tag. He probably already bought his ticket." I felt really awkward standing in front of my parents while they stared at me. I think they saw that, because my dad patted a place beside him and said, "Come sit down and let's work this out."

"What do *you* think you should do?" Mom asked me.

"Well... I should give back the money, but I don't have it. Maybe I can offer to work at the store until I pay it back?" I said without real conviction. I really didn't have much time to work, except maybe one evening a week. That would take me forever to pay them back. Suddenly I had an idea.

"Hey! Maybe I can tell them I'll work in the summer and pay them when I get the money. Only...they would have to wait almost a year for that," I finished uncertainly.

"Hmm," Dad rubbed his chin, "it's not a bad plan, but I don't think it's fair for the store to have to wait a year to get their money back. What if that fifty was important for them to order new stock to sell, and now they couldn't do it because they were short fifty? No, we can't let someone else suffer because of our own faults."

We sat thinking. I no longer felt so lousy. I'd told my parents what I had done, and here we were brainstorming for a solution. This wasn't so bad. It was hard, but it felt *right.*

"Uh, Dad? Mom?" I started tentatively, "Could you...would it be possible...I mean, would you lend me the money to pay back the store and I'll work babysitting during Chol HaMoed to pay *you* back? I know we're not supposed to work during Chol

HaMoed if we can help it, but if I babysit or work as a mother's helper, then I can help someone else relax more during that time. That would be okay, right?"

My parents looked at each other and did that silent communication thing again.

I saw a tiny bit of a smile in my mother's eyes.

"That would work," Dad nodded.

"And I did hear," Mom added with a twinkle in her eye, "that the Schechter's are looking for someone to go with them to help watch their kids at Hershey Park. Perhaps you can call them and see if they could use your help."

"Wow! That would be awesome! I can take Yaakov and Shoshana on the rides while their mom takes care of the baby!" It was my perfect job scenario. I would be helping and having fun at the same time.

"Or, their mom might want you to stay with the baby and walk him around in the carriage while *she* goes on the rides with her children," Mom said with raised eyebrows.

"Oh, right," I sighed. "Either way, it would be an all-day job and I could earn practically everything I owe in one day. And I really wouldn't mind pushing the baby around. Can I go call them right now?" I was instantly excited.

"Not so fast," Dad put a hand on my shoulder, "we still have a few things to address." My enthusiasm deflated like a balloon letting out all the air.

"Um...what else?" I asked. Dad was quiet, so I thought a bit and said, "I have to take care of returning the money right away?"

"That's right," Dad said. "And, I think you need to apologize. Teshuva is realizing your mistakes, and ...?"

"And saying you're sorry and then doing the right thing!" I said with confidence.

"So...?" Mom prompted.

"I have to bring the money back to the cashier and...and tell her I'm sorry," I worked out slowly. "Do I need to apologize to the store manager too?"

"That might not be a bad idea, since many days have passed and the owner is missing that money and the cashier probably took the blame. You need to set things straight and make sure the owner knows she wasn't at fault."

I nodded, but I felt kinda scared. What would the owner say? Would he yell at me? Would the cashier blame me for stealing? I really didn't want to do it.

Why was facing up to what I did wrong so hard and so complicated? I had to tell my parents, I had to tell the cashier and apologize, I had to speak with the storeowner and apologize. I had to earn back the money. All this for just keeping the money that someone else gave me by mistake. If I had just been straight and given the money back immediately, none of this would have happened.

"I guess I should give the money back right now?" I asked.

"That would be best," Dad said. "Never put off doing what you should...especially if it is teshuva. Especially when you have wronged someone else and need to make it right."

"Would you drive me and come with me when I talk to them?" I would feel better with my dad's support.

"Sure, we'll both come with you, come on!" Dad stood up and took out his wallet. He removed fifty dollars and handed them to me. "Here you go," he said and looked over at my mom, who had been writing something on a pad of paper.

"And to make it official, sign this," Mom said, handing me the sheet she tore off the pad. I looked at what she had written: *I, Yosef Shalom, agree to pay my parents the sum of $50, which they have loaned me. I will work during Chol HaMoed Succos and, if necessary, any other available time to earn the money to pay them back.* My mom had printed my name under a line for me to sign my name on, with a space for the date.

"Sign this and date it and we will have a real contract between us," said Mom.

I took the pen from her and looked at the paper. *I, Yosef Shalom, agree to pay my parents the sum of $50 which they have loaned me....* I signed it and put in the date, feeling like I had grown up quite a bit.

I gave her the page and sighed with relief, heading for the door. We all trooped into the car and drove the short distance to Kosher Mart. When we got there, I took the fifty dollars, marched up to the cashier I had used and, as soon as she finished with her customer, presented her with the money saying, "I'm sorry, but you accidentally gave me fifty dollars extra with my change a few days ago. I should have given it back right away, but here it is. I hope you didn't get into trouble because of it."

The cashier stared at the money for a moment and then looked at me with wonder on her face.

"Oh, thank you!" she sounded almost like she was about to cry. "I had to give my own money to make the tally balance at the end of the day. I couldn't figure out how I miscounted fifty dollars. You are so brave and honest to come and give me this money. Thank you, and bless you! Maybe the manager will not be so angry with me when I tell him."

"Don't worry about that," I said, now sorrier than ever that I had kept the money. I wanted to fix what I had caused. "I'll talk to the manager. Where is he?" She told us where his office was and I knocked on his door. I was so intent on making sure the cashier wasn't taking the blame for my actions, that I forgot to be shy or scared. When I heard, "Come in," I just marched into the office and walked up to the big man sitting behind the desk.

"Are you Mr. Stein?" I asked him, "The manager?" The man looked at me and then my parents inquiringly.

"Yes, what can I do for you, young man?"

I explained what had happened and ended with, "...so you see, it wasn't your cashier's fault at all. I shouldn't have kept the money. I'm really sorry to have caused so much trouble. I gave her back the fifty, and I hope you don't blame her."

The man smiled and nodded at me. "What is your name?"

"Yosef," I told him.

"Well, Yosef, I can see you are growing into a real ben Torah. It must have been really hard to give back such a nice amount of money." He looked at my parents and added, "You are doing a wonderful job with this young one. I would be proud to have a son like him."

We spoke for a few more minutes and Mr. Stein shook my hand and thanked me again.

On the way home from the market, a thought occurred to me.

"Hey, I still have the tickets! What do I do about those? Can we go to the concert, or...or should I lose that privilege because I got the money for them in the wrong way?" I really hoped my parents wouldn't agree to that second part, but I knew it was a possibility. Better to get it out there.

"Well, I don't know...what do you think Mom?" my dad asked looking at my mom.

"Hmm. We *did* say Yossi had to earn the money himself to pay for concert tickets. And, although this is upside down and backwards, he *will* in effect be working for the money, sooo...."

"We can go?" I blurted excitedly.

"Before we make that final decision...let me ask you this. What do you think Hashem's answer to your tefilah was?"

I didn't need to think about it. I knew. "Hashem wanted me to learn how to really do teshuva before Yom Kippur. And...I think...in a very strange way, even though I didn't do it right at first, he knew I would figure out what I *should* do. And then, well, in the end I kind of get a happy hug from Hashem because I did what brings me closer to Him. Keeping His Torah. Being yashar (straight—righteous) and not stealing.

"A happy hug from Hashem?" my dad asked.

"Well, a happy, you-did-good-and-now-you-can-go-to-the-concert hug?"

My parents laughed heartily. "We are so proud of you!" they said. "And, yes, we will go to this concert. After all, we are all in this learning thing together."

My Truth

Menucha is the new girl at Bais Bnos. Things get sticky when she takes on more than she can handle.

Everyone knew sixth grader Ariella Gross, the most organized and popular class representative at Bais Bnos. She seemed to do everything, from helping teachers hand out class notices to running errands to the front office. She even took her leadership one step further. Ariella made sure that all the girls in her class had good notes. I think that's one reason why the teachers liked her so much and nominated her for class representative. When girls were absent or slow note takers, Ariella made sure there were copies from someone who took good notes. Ariella was proud of that, and was given permission to use the school copy machine. I don't know how, but Ariella could get a lot of things done.

In between classes one day, as I passed by the copy room, I noticed a girl from our class using the machine while Ariella stood by her side. "Make sure the book is turned sideways so we don't miss the edges of the notes," I heard her instruct. "Okay, just keep doing that and then bring them to me when you've finished all eighteen pages." *Maybe that's how she gets so much done,* I thought to myself. *She had others do some of the work.* Later in class I saw Ariella hand Devorah the batch of copied notes and say, "Here you are. All the notes you missed while you were absent."

How does Ariella pick the girls to make copies? I wondered. *Well, most kids wouldn't say no to her if she asked them to help. Everyone likes being a part of what she does.*

A few months later I realized that I was having some trouble seeing the board. My doctor told me I'd need to get glasses, but until I went for my appointment, I asked to be moved closer to the front of the room. And wouldn't you know it, but our teacher changed my seat to the front row, right next to Ariella's.

"Hey, Menucha," Ariella's smile seemed kind and inviting.

"I can finally see the board," I said. I took a deep breath. "It's great up here."

"Welcome to a front row seat." She smiled, then looked me up and down and continued, "I'm glad you're here. I need someone to help me at break. I have some papers that need copying for Devorah, who was out sick again, and Shira, who's a slower note taker."

Before I could answer, the teacher began an intense math lesson, so I didn't say a word. Anyhow, I didn't know how to answer Ariella. I mean, it was a bit odd for her to assign me a job without asking me if I even wanted to help. I didn't like being bossed around and I began to feel sorry that I had ever changed seats. But since I was new here and a bit shy, and since all the girls seemed to know each other, I figured that doing some volunteer work for Ariella might be one way I could make friends and do a chesed (kind deed) at the same time.

When the bell rang, Ariella reminded me that we were heading to the copy machine to make copies of her notes. As we walked by her desk in the main office, the secretary turned to us and smiled, "Help yourself to the copier, no one's using it."

"This is Menucha," Ariella said, as she put her arm around my shoulders. It was as if we had been best friends since kindergarten. "She's helping me out with the class makeup notes."

Ariella stopped at the machine, turned it on, and showed me how to use it. Next thing I knew, she was thrusting her notebook at me. "Copy pages 10 to 31." She winked at me and left the room. *Where's she going?* I thought, as I leaned over and twisted my neck to see her. I saw her schmoozing with another girl in the hallway.

I stood for a minute, dumbfounded, then began flipping through Ariella's thick blue binder, placing it page by page on the copier and pressing the little green start button. I felt put upon; I didn't like being told to do something while Ariella went off to do what she pleased. And twenty-one pages of notes—wasn't that a bit much? *I'll only do this today,* I thought to myself. *Ariella will have to find someone else to help out tomorrow! Why did she boss people around like this? Why doesn't she do the copying? Well, I hope that I at least make some friends out of this job.* I bit my lip. Fifteen more pages to copy, and it was almost time for me to be back in class. The bell rang just as I finished the last page of copying, and Ariella returned.

"Good," she said, with a big smile. "You've done this so quickly; you'll help me tomorrow as well. Hand me my binder; we've got to get to English class."

I was following Ariella when a group of girls came up to us and said, "Hi." I smiled, and Ariella, the girls, and I chatted. We walked into the class and two more girls stopped and spoke with us.

When I got home from school that day, I felt out of sorts. I plopped myself down on the bed and thought, *why didn't I just say no to Ariella?* Then I thought about all of those girls coming up and saying hi and talking with me when I was with her. That felt so good. *See, I'm getting more popular.* So, maybe I'll stick it out and be the copier person for a bit.

A few weeks went by, and Ariella had me at the copy machine at least four more times. I dutifully copied her notes, and each time Ariella and I would hang out with her friends.

It was around that time that I really began to enjoy math. I had learned many of the lessons in my old school, so my notes were pretty organized and up-to-date. "Your notes are so clear!" Ariella noticed as she glanced at my desk. "That's perfect! We'll use your notes in our math note gemach, right?" she told me after class.

"Math note gemach?" I had never heard that term before.

"Yes," she continued. "Since our class is fast-paced and not everyone takes notes as well as you do, we'll start a new gemach." She paused, "It'll be *your* notes that help everyone keep up. Isn't that wonderful!"

I smiled. A compliment from the most popular girl felt good.

"And every day we can make at least four copies of your notes because I know that there are some in the class that could really use them. If anyone is out sick, we can make more." Ariella smiled.

"So, you want to use my notes and copy them?" I wondered whom Ariella would ask to do that.

"Sure!" Ariella looked into my eyes with her deep brown ones. "You'll make four copies of your notes every day. It's a chesed." She smiled and turned around in her seat to face Miriam.

As they began chatting quietly I thought to myself, *I guess I'm getting more popular here at school—and it is doing chesed.* So I went along with it.

But as time passed, I found myself standing in the copy room day after day, copying and stapling my notes for the math note gemach, while the rest of the class was either outside or hanging out in the break room between classes. Right after class, I would scoot to the copy room, waving at the secretary as I breezed pass.

"Back so soon?" "Again?" and "Did you even leave?" she would quip.

A gnawing feeling was growing in my stomach. *Why did I have to miss recess? Was this the best way for me to make friends? Yes, it was,* I told myself. *You are doing a great mitzvah. The ones getting the notes will be grateful for your efforts and like you more.*

But it wasn't working out that way. I spent way too much time in the copy room.

"Thanks, Menucha," Ariella said casually as I walked into class with a stack of papers.

"These will be helpful," added the math teacher.

"No problem," I said with a smile.

After Rochel missed three days of school, she found me in the hallway by my locker and asked me if I could get her my math notes from the beginning of the week. During break time I was busy copying even more notes, and I had to skip most of lunch to get it all done.

The next Monday, Chaya asked me for copies of Friday's math class that she had missed—she had been out sick. I looked around the class to see the girls all chatting with one another, and I felt so alone. "Sure, I'll take care of it at break." *What a lie,* I thought to myself. *I hate this.*

"Thanks," Chaya smiled and immediately turned to join a group of her friends. I just stood there and muttered, "Yeah, no problem."

How could Ariella dump her chesed on me? Where was she anyhow? I looked around and saw her laughing with Rochel. Why was I doing all the work?

"Great job, Menucha!" Ariella said on another day, as she saw the pile of notes that I had copied and organized. "I'll take those." She grabbed the pile from me just as the teacher entered the room.

I sat in my seat, ready for class, but I didn't feel well. As I put my head down on my desk, a thought flew into my mind: *I HATE copying. I hate spending so much of my free time doing things...alone. But it's a mitzvah, isn't it? Shouldn't I feel good doing it?*

Just then our teacher, Mrs. Blum, looked at me and asked, "Are you okay?"

"Not really," I answered in a muffled voice.

Mrs. Blum put her hand on my shoulder and guided me into the hallway. "Class, please open up to chapter 14 and read to yourselves, I'll be right back."

The next thing I knew, Mrs. Blum and I were standing in the hallway facing each other. "Menucha, Ariella's told me that you've been copying your math notes every day for the gemach?"

"Yes, it's ... a chesed," I spoke softly.

"I've been meaning to talk to you about that." Mrs. Blum paused and I looked at her blue eyes. I never realized how pretty they were up close. "I'm a friend of Ruthie's who works in the front office. She told me the other day that you miss your breaks to constantly copy notes for the girls. She's worried about you."

I nodded slowly waiting for Mrs. Blum to continue. "Maybe you're overdoing it. What do you think?"

"So, what do I do? Ariella practically put me in charge of the math note gemach?" I looked up at my teacher and shrugged.

"You tell Ariella the truth," she told me. "It's not fair to put such a task on one girl. This is a job that can be divided up amongst all of you—especially those girls who are asking for the notes. Why do you think they haven't offered to help you?"

"Well," I felt torn inside, "I told them I was happy to do it, because...aren't we supposed to *want* to do mitzvos and be happy about it? And..."

"Yes?" Mrs. Blum gently prompted.

"I just wanted them to like me. I'm new in the school and I thought if I was helpful and did chesed, I'd have more friends."

"And does that seem to be happening?"

"Not really," I sighed. "I'm too busy making copies to hang out with anyone much."

Mrs. Blum nodded. "You've kind of mixed up the idea of doing chesed because it is Hashem's derech and doing something to gain friends. But, you *can* do both if you include others in your mitzvah. So...?"

"But, Ariella's the one..."

"Didn't she put you in charge of the gemach?" Mrs. Blum interrupted.

My eyes opened wide with realization. "I can give the notes to whoever asks for them and tell *them* to make copies!"

"That is certainly one option," Mrs. Blum nodded. "I'm sure if you give it a bit of thought, you can come up with a way to take the burden off your shoulders and let others participate in this effort, hmm?"

I smiled in relief. "Yes!"

I suddenly felt light, almost like I could jump up and fly.

"And, think of it this way, sooner or later the girls will pick up on you're not being happy. *That's* not how to win over friends," Mrs. Blum added. "Let's go to class. I'll meet with you and Ariella afterwards to make a plan, right?"

"Thank you, Mrs. Blum! That would be great!"

So, after class Mrs. Blum asked Ariella to stay a few minutes and I explained the problem. I told Ariella that I had taken on more than I could handle with the note gemach and the copying. I told Ariella that I was going to spread the job out amongst the other girls.

Ariella seemed almost shocked. "But you gave me the impression that you liked it," she said, shaking her head, "And it's kind of nice to just have the notes there for us when we need them, instead of having to go copy them. What if I help out more?" Ariella continued. "It's a real chesed, you know."

But I stayed strong. "Ariella, I haven't been honest with you." I looked down at the linoleum tiles on the floor. "I haven't been honest with myself either. I don't want to do it. At least, not by myself."

"I'm sorry, Menucha, if I pushed you into this job. Is that what happened?"

"I thought I was doing a mitzvah," I said. "But, I ended up resenting the job. I guess I just wanted to be liked." I lifted my eyes towards Ariella.

"I'm really sorry, Menucha. What should we do now?" Ariella looked at Mrs. Blum and at me. Mrs. Blum gave me a little nod.

"Um…how about making a rotation? Each day of the week it would be a different person's responsibility to make copies," I suggested.

"And I'm not sure notes are needed every day." Mrs. Blum added. "Math is something you learn through doing. So, I'll help you out by indicating when notes would be helpful for those who have been absent or are having trouble. Otherwise, the students will come to me for help. How does that sound?"

I nodded with relief. "That would be great!"

"Perfect!" Ariella agreed. "I should have done some of this in the beginning. I just didn't pay attention to how much time it would take for one person to be in charge of it."

"And Ariella, it's a wonderful thing to come up with ways to help others," Mrs. Blum told her, "but if you always assign others to do the actual helping, you don't get a feel for what kind of effort it requires. Since you are a real idea person when it comes to doing chesed, I suggest that in the future you begin by doing whatever you devise through your own efforts, and then enlist help when needed.

Ariella smiled and nodded, "That makes sense; I will." She turned to me and said, "I seriously didn't realize how much you disliked doing this job—but, honestly, now that I really think about it, I guess anyone would resent taking all their free time to just copy notes. I'm really sorry. I'll be more careful in the future."

"Thanks!" I took a big breath. "Whew! I feel great finally speaking up!" Our meeting ended, and Mrs. Blum thanked both of us for "going the extra mile," as she put it, for the school.

The next day when I arrived at our first class, I saw Ariella waving a list with the names of volunteers for making copies. I went over to her and mentioned that I could use a set of Chumash notes, because I hadn't taken the best notes the day before. Ariella added me to the list with Chaya, who was out sick. At break, I watched a girl named Elisheva head toward the copy machine, while I went and talked with a few of the girls. After break I thanked both Ariella and Elisheva, and I smiled to myself, feeling free and strong because I knew now that I could speak up for myself and do the right thing for the right reason.

Fun & Facts

Midvar Sheker Tirchak – מדבר שקר תרחק

Stay far away from falsehood (lying).

The Torah tells us to distance ourselves from untruths (*Shemos* 23:7).

We are not permitted to listen to words that we know are false or to spread that information.

Word clues:
Ever try to balance on one foot? What about on one foot while on tiptoe? Did you know that just by looking at the Hebrew letters that spell "falsehood" and "truth"—in the script they appear in the Torah—we can learn about the meaning of the words? In Hebrew, שקר–*sheker; shin, kuf, reish*–means "lie, or falsehood." Lying or cheating (another form of lying), does not leave us balanced. We are not on solid ground.

Take a look at the Hebrew letters in the form they appear in the hand-written letters of the Torah. There is a clue to the meaning of the word in the way the letters are formed.

Shin, kuf, reish: notice that the ש sits on its tiny point, unbalanced on the baseline.

The ק descends below the baseline and is unbalanced on one "foot."

The ר also stands on one foot, without a left leg, also leaving it without a solid "footing."

Sheker—lying and cheating do not leave us balanced on solid ground.

On the other hand, *all three letters of* אמת—*emes,* truth, *aleph, mem, sav,* rest on "solid footing." The letters have strong bases, each having two feet. The Talmud teaches us that truth can stand, balanced and strong, but falsehood and lies cannot.

Did you know?

Medical student and police officer John Larson invented the polygraph, or lie detector, in 1921. The machine records the physical responses a person has to specific questions. These responses include rate of breathing, heart rate, blood pressure, and sweat on the fingertips. There is much controversy regarding the use of polygraph tests in courts and other legal situations, because subjects can learn how to outsmart them. They are still sometimes used in courts of law, but usually are not considered absolute, valid evidence.

Question: Why do people lie?

Possible answer: To get on someone's good side, or to get ahead in life, as when someone lies about their education to get a better job or to impress friends. Those lies might work for a while, until the lie is discovered. Do you think someone who lies feels good about himself? How does someone who lies feel about the one they are lying to? Do they respect them?

INSIGHT FROM THE CIA

How do you know if someone is lying?

The CIA, or Central Intelligence Agency, is the foreign intelligence service of the US government. People who work for the CIA must become experts in finding out the truth. The safety of our country may be at risk if, for example, someone is pretending to work for the United States when they are actually spying for another country. People who work for the CIA have to undergo many lie detector tests themselves, helping CIA agents to become experts in detecting lies. Here is advice from three former CIA officers who wrote, *Spy the Lie,*[1] in which they teach us ways to tell if someone is lying.

TMI (too much information) — People who lie may answer questions with too much information. For example, when asked at the airport what is in his suitcase, a person might list all of the contents and then go into a long story about how their aunt bought them one item, and how they got another one on sale. Of course, people might also do this when they are simply very friendly and talkative.

Too Polite — Another way to tell if someone is lying is by listening to the way they answer questions. If they interrupt an interview to suddenly say, "Oh, by the way, that's a nice shirt you are wearing today," they may be trying to distract the interviewer from noticing a lie by being overly polite and complimenting something about them. Of course, they could also just really like that tie.

Complaining — Sometimes when a person is asked a question, to avoid telling the truth he or she will complain that the questions are taking too long or they might ask why the person needs to know such information. Again, this might also be true of someone in a rush or lacking in patience.

I already told you — Even if they haven't already told the interviewer something, they may say that they have to confuse the person asking the questions. If they are in a rush, they might be impatient with more questions. Impatience is not lying.

Throat clearing or swallowing — A nervous or anxious person may clear his or her throat loudly or swallow with a gulp before answering a question. Then again, they might also just have congestion from allergies or a cold.

Touching the face — A person may touch his or her face, ear, or nose before or while answering questions. This might also be a sign of nervousness.

Cleaning up or making oneself neater — When asked a question they don't want to answer, people will brush off dirt from their pants, straighten their shirts, or fix their hair. That doesn't necessarily mean they are lying. It could just be they are uncomfortable with what is being asked.

[1]Philip Houston, Michael Floyd, Susan Carnicero and Don Tennant, *Spy the Lie* (New York:, St. Martin's Press, 2012), Chapter 5.

While all of these behaviors might point to lying, they could just as well point to someone who is uncomfortable at being questioned or singled out. While a skilled investigator might use some of these pointers to reveal lying, it takes training and experience to truly determine if someone is lying or just nervous. Often a person might be nervous at being found out for something totally unrelated to what they are being asked about. It is important to keep in mind that doing any of the above is not automatically and positively a sign of lying.

Think:

Even if you get away with a lie, how does it make you feel inside? You might avoid a scolding or even punishment, but does it really help you? Do you feel good about yourself?

Cool Fact:

People who consistently tell lies eventually lose the ability to care about what is true and what is not. Often, they no longer know what is real and what is false.

Remember:
One's neshama cannot be fooled and cannot be harmed, but we *can* throw so much mud over it—build such a barrier to it—that we have trouble accessing it.

Someone who has lost the sense of truth has to make the *decision* to always tell the truth and be meticulous about it. Eventually that sense, that queasy, uncomfortable feeling one gets when he lies, the neshama's warning, will return as the pathway to the neshama is cleared away by our righteous, truthful behavior.

Bonus Section

FOR KIDS, PARENTS, TEACHERS AND COUNSELORS...

Fun, Interesting, Engaging Activities for Camp, School, the Shabbos Table and Parties

Activities to Promote the Mitzvah of Ve'ahavta Lereacha Kamocha

ואהבתה לרעך כמוך

Love Your Friend As You Love Yourself

When you really try to get to know and understand another person, you learn to appreciate them and to accept them. That is how you can come to love them. If we all do this, we will have unity—achdus, amongst klal Yisroel. We will stand up for each other. When we have unity, we have shalom—peace.

Games that promote Achdus

1. **The I Like This About You Game:**

   Supplies needed: pencil, pen, construction paper cut into hearts, triangles, or other geometric shapes large enough to write 3-4 sentences.

   - This activity requires an even number of participants. Split the group in half and make an "A" group and a "B" group. Each person in A will be paired up with a B partner. The group leader will supply the geometric papers. Have each partner write *"I like this about you:"* at the top of the paper. Then write a list of things they like about the other person and sign their name. When done, partners should exchange papers. This can be done several times by reassigning partners and having them write about the new partner. At the end, participants will have a collection of cards with things others appreciate about them.

- Variation: have each participant write a list of positive qualities about the other person using the letters from their name. This is called an acrostic. An example is RINA: **R**eal, **I**ntelligent, **N**ice, **A**thletic. Or, to make it more relevant, use phrases such as: **R**eally thoughtful, **I**nteresting and **I**ntelligent, **N**ever gets upset, **A**lways helpful.

- Alternative to letting participants keep the cards: take a hole puncher and make holes in the tops of the papers. String a ribbon through the papers to connect them, and hang them in the classroom, lunchroom, or bunkhouse. (When notes are to be displayed, don't have the participants sign them so that they are not embarrassed to have their notes made public.)

. **The Secret Admirer:**

Supplies needed: Paper bag, small pieces of paper, pen/pencil.

- Write participants names on pieces of paper and place into a paper bag. Each person will pull out a name from the bag and become the *secret admirer* of the person whose name they selected.

- For one week, the secret admirer will think of little acts of kindness for the person they chose. Examples: leaving the person a note with a compliment, a good thought or a funny joke, leaving small gifts (snacks, stickers, etc.), providing lesson notes their selected person might have missed when they were absent, leaving a box or packet of tissues on their desk if they have a cold.

- Make sure that the admirers and partners remain anonymous for the designated amount of time. Have a party at the end with heart shaped or happy faced cookies and announce the partners. Have each pair share with the group what they did for each other or what they liked most that was done for them.

3. **Pat on the back game:**

Supplies needed: 4x5 or 8x10 cardstock or heavy weight paper, with the words, "Thank you for:" written at the top, fine-tipped markers, tape.

- Each participant will have a card taped to his back. For 30 minutes participants will walk around the room and write a continuation of the"*Thank you for...*" sentence about the person wearing the card (directly onto the card on his back), then move on to the next person until the time is up. Participants should write something they are thankful *that* person did or said, not a general thanks for things.

- At the end of 30 minutes, everyone pulls off their cards and reads them. To gain greater impact, have everyone sit in a circle and pass their card to the person on their right, and then have each person read the paper they hold, out loud.

. **Relay Races:**

The goal of these activities is to make it clear that we need each Jew in Klal Yisroel and that everyone has an important part to play in our nation.

These are a set of relay races for which participants can only earn a prize if everyone participates and completes their part of the activities. (Prizes to be designated by a teacher or group leader.)

For large groups, divide participants amongst different tables or areas and assign each one a race. For smaller groups, have participants sit together in one area.

All activities are to continue until everyone at the table completes the activity.

Supplies needed are specified for each race.

Table Relay Races

- Balance a book on your head and pass a pencil to the person on your right without the book falling off, then pass the book as well so that he or she can repeat the process with the person on the right.
- Put a glove on and off, pass it to the person on your right.
- Balance a raw egg on a spoon, pass it from hand to hand, then pass it to the next person without dropping the egg.

- Hit a balloon in the air, passing it on to the next person.
- Provide everyone with straws. Using the straw, blow a balled up little piece of paper to the person on your right. Try to get the paper around to the first person within a set period of time.
- Place a bowl of beads in the center of the table. With a string knotted at one end, have each person add a bead to the string until a necklace or bracelet is completed. Optionally, race to see which group gets the most done in a given period of time. (Note: this can be done as a chesed project to make bracelets for kids who are sick or in some form of need.)
- Sign your name on a paper and pass it to the next person.
- Pass a ball backwards over your head to the next person—don't turn your head to look!

➥ Kids will cheer each other on, as they hope each one completes their part of the race, in order to win the group prize. When they have completed the race, point out that, because they knew each person's job was important in the race and that their own prize depended on it, they were encouraging and caring toward others.

➥ Explain that everyone has something to contribute to Klal Yisroel, and by encouraging each other and helping everyone to do their best, we all benefit because we all receive Hashem's brachos together. Hashem wants us to care for each other, and He gives our whole nation His brachos when we listen to Him and do His mitzvos.

5. **Pass the Baton**
   - Have the leader do something that is clearly an act of caring toward another (give someone a hand with what they are doing, give them a better chair, help someone find a seat).
   - Explain that you have done an act of ahavas Yisroel and are passing this baton (it can be made of cardboard) on to the next person. It is the baton of ahavas Yisroel. Explain that you are marking the baton with your initials.
   - When the person getting the baton does an act of kindness or caring for someone, he or she should add his or her initials to the baton and pass it on to another person.
   - When everyone has had a turn using the baton, it can be put on display in a prominent place. Seeing this baton encourages everyone to "cheer on" their peers by caring about them and passing on the baton.

Activities to Prevent Lashon Hora

1. **The Danger of Lashon Hora—Part I**

   The goal of this activity is to demonstrate how lashon hora spreads very quickly, and that it is hard to take back words of lashon hora once they are spoken.

   - Distribute a large amount of craft feathers to each person. If possible, give each person a different color. (Alternatively, hand out feather-sized pieces of tissue paper.)

- Instruct them to count their feathers or tissue paper snips, and then place them in a container. Go outside and have them scatter their feathers or tissue papers.
- After a significant amount of time (it could be a few hours or the following day), have the participants return to try and collect the same amount of feathers or papers they scattered. If they were given a specific color, instruct them to gather *only* their color.

➥ Everyone will realize that the feathers moved since they were scattered, and some may have blown away. When they see that they are unable to collect the same amount that they scattered, you can teach them the lesson that lashon hora spreads quickly and is hard to take back.

➥ Share the famous story of a woman who went to a rav and asked him what she could do to take back the lashon hora she had spoken. The rav instructed her to cut open her feather pillows and scatter the feathers throughout town. She did this and returned to the rav. He told her to go back and pick up all the feathers. When she found this impossible the rav taught her this very lesson.

2. **The Danger of Lashon Hora—Part II**

The goal of this activity is to teach that when we speak lashon hora our zechuyos, the merits we gain from good deeds, are transferred to the person we speak lashon hora about.

- Distribute a sticker to each participant.
- Tell them we are playing the "No" game, in which no one is allowed to say the word "no" for a few hours. This should

include all forms of "no," such as "not," "uh, uh," and "don't."

- Anyone who says "no" has to give their sticker to the person to whom they said "no."

➥ It is likely that stickers will be transferred between the kids several times. Teach them that it was hard to hold back from saying "no"—a negative word—even when we were conscious of trying hard not to say it.

➥ Think of how many negative words we say throughout our day when we are *not* conscious of trying hard to hold back, and realize that our zechuyos are transferred just as quickly as the stickers.

CAUTION: Participants should not use the "no" game in any way that will tease or make someone uncomfortable. Neither should one use tricks to *try* to get another to say "no". This defeats the purpose of promoting ahavas Yisroel.

3. **Fire Extinguishers: How not to listen to lashon hora**

Lashon hora is like a dangerous fire that can destroy. Sometimes, though, it seems impossible to avoid hearing lashon hora if it's being spoken around us.

For example, several kids might be seated in the back of a car. One of the kids might begin speaking negatively about a classmate. A second person might add a few more negative comments. The third innocent bystander might not want to hear the negative speech. But they are trapped in the car. What can be done?

Here are some tips. We call them FIRE EXTINGUISHERS because they are phrases that we can practice and can use to put out the fire of lashon hora.

Fire Extinguishers:

1. Change the topic: by asking a general question. “Hey, does anyone know when Rosh Chodesh falls out?” Or “When does the pizza shop close on Motzei Shabbos?”
2. Divert the conversation: “Oh, I think there might be a bug on the floor.” (There might or might not, but it’s a good distractor.)
3. With action: quickly drop some money on the ground or floor and say, “Oy, I dropped my money.”
4. Directly: “Let’s talk about something else, this might be lashon hora.”
5. Tell a joke you know: such as “Hey guys, what do you call a fake noodle? An Impasta!”
6. Say, “I’m trying to watch my speech as a zechus (merit) for...name a choleh (sick person) or someone who needs a zechus. Can we talk about something else?”

Make up your own Fire Extinguishers:

1. Print *Fire Extinguishers* on a large poster board. Then have the class make suggestions about possible ways to put out the fire of lashon horah. List their suggestions on the poster board.

2. Divide up into groups and role-play. One person pretends to be the person about to speak lashon hora.

He should do so by introducing the topic, rather than actually saying lashon hora. For instance, say, "Do I have something juicy to tell you..." or "Guess what I heard about a teacher on my way in to school?"

3. The second person chooses one or more of the *fire extinguisher* responses and practices responding to the speaker.
4. Switch roles.

Activities to Help Promote Gratitude and Curb Jealousy

1. **Todah L'Hashem Activity:**

The goal of this activity is to have participants think of things they can be grateful for, and to take the time to express their gratitude to Hashem. Appreciating what we do have, and that it all comes from Hashem, takes the focus away from what we don't have.

- Wrap a big box in nice wrapping paper and a bow.
- Cut a slit in the top, large enough to be able to easily drop cards inside.
- Distribute pretty or interesting "Thank You" cards.
- Encourage kids to fill out the cards and drop them in the box every day.
- Once a week, empty the box and share what was written on the different cards.

2. **On-the-Lookout Detectives**

- Have every participant keep a small notebook. Explain that they are detectives, on the lookout for qualities people have that are gifts from Hashem. At first it will seem like there isn't that much to notice but, after a while, they will be amazed to see that they are filling up their notebooks.

- When they notice someone being clever, artistic, agile, especially good in sports, math or some other area, they should note it in their notebook.

➥ Since all our talents and strengths come from Hashem, we can realize that we all have exactly what we are supposed to have. Let's notice those positive qualities in each other.

Notebook entries might look something like this:

November 5th: *Noticed Avrami is able to finish his math sheet faster than anyone else. That is a gift from Hashem.*

December 7th: *Yael was picked for a solo dance in this year's school-wide performance. At first it seemed unfair, but when I saw her dance, I knew it was the right thing, because she was amazing! It is really fun to see someone do something so well. I realize that Hashem gives us gifts for our own benefit and for others to gain from as well.*

December 21st: *Rabbi Z. looks tired today. But he is still smiling and showing us how to tie tzizis. Hashem has gifted him with patience even when he probably doesn't feel so well.*

January 9th: *Noticed Yaakov helping Zack bring more chairs into the room. Thank you Hashem for giving them the ability to be helpful.*

Activities to Help Promote Honesty

1. **The True or False Game**

- One participant will stand up and tell the group three short stories about him/herself.
- Two of the stories will be true, and one will not. The group will vote on which of the stories they think are true. The majority wins.
- The storyteller will then tell everyone which story was false. This game can be played until all members have had a chance to share.

➥ By trying to guess which story truly fits the person telling it, people will learn that while sometimes an untruth is easy to spot, at other times it can be very difficult.

2. **The Button Game**

Similar to the "Who Took the Cookie from the Cookie Jar" game, the button game requires four to eight people and a button.

- The button is passed in cupped hands from person to person while one individual, the "seeker," stands with their back turned away, (so as not to see what the others are doing), and counts to 10.
- Once the "seeker" finishes counting, he or she turns around and is allowed to ask three people in the group if

they have the button. If asked, the person has to be honest and either says he doesn't have it or reveals the button.

- If none of the three have the button, the one who does then shows that he has it.
- Whoever has the button becomes the next "seeker."

Resources For Games:

*Chaya Kruk, Baltimore, MD for helping to create the Fire Extinguisher lesson.

*Talya Turk, Bnos Yisroel, Baltimore, MD for submitting the Achdus Awareness, Activity Races, Toda L'Hashem and Shmiras Halashon Activities.

Acknowledgments

Hakaras HaTov

From Danielle Sarah Storch

My deepest gratitude is extended to the Ahavas Yisrael Project and to founder Rebbetzin Tzippora Harris and Director, Rebbetzin Leah Greenman who have started me on the original journey of loving my fellow Jew the Torah way. It is this project that provided the original sparks for this book. I am truly blessed to thank my support team, "Team Storch": my dedicated husband, Frank, and my children, Shulamis Tova and Yosef Binyamin, for their constant feedback; my loving mother-in-law, Mrs. Hannah Storch; and my most wonderful parents, Dr. Linda and Mr. Larry Nieman. A thank-you to Mrs. Chana Feiga Seigel and Aidel Cooperman who helped keep this project alive. Thank you to my chavrusa, Marcel Ariel for her daily inspiration. A big thank you to Cousin Henya Storch for her guidance and support, and to Mrs. Judy Sandman for her excellent editing skills.

I am very happy to thank Mrs. Chaya Kruk for teaching me the importance of bringing Hashem into the picture when working on ahavas Yisrael. May Hashem bless you and your entire family with great health and long life.

I am privileged to be a bas Yisroel in this generation, whose strong desire it is to see the Jewish people united with Moshiach. The children are our future, and stories help to shape us. With that in mind, *Step into My Shoes* was created to teach ahavas Yisroel. When the Jewish people unite, we merit G-d's full protection and blessings. It is my wish to see that speedily in our day.

From Tova NessAiver

Hakadosh Baruch Hu has blessed me with the opportunity to be a partner in the writing of this book, and I am thankful for all the wonderful individuals who helped bring it to fruition.

With special kavod to my parents, Rabbi Levi Ness, zt"l, and Devorah (Debi) Ness and my "Uncle," David Ness, zt"l—you gave me life and unshakable awareness of Hashem.

I owe a deep debt of gratitude to Rabbi Yaakov Hopfer of Baltimore's Shearith Israel Congregation, whose divrei Torah, insight, and guidance helped mold my perception of what halacha is, and by his example showed me how kindness, compassion and understanding guide every nuance of a Torah life.

A heartfelt thank you to all those whose thoughts, suggestions, and editing have helped hone the material and presentation of this book:

To my accomplished son-in-law, Daniel Mozes, who was willing to contribute his eagle eye for detail and accuracy (along with a sharp wit) and allocate his much-in-demand time to editing—and making me laugh. To my wonderfully talented daughter, Eliana, his wife, for helping with suggestions, advice, and formatting as well as working on cover design possibilities—and for lending her husband's time to the project.

To my incredibly gifted daughter, Tziona, for her cover design suggestions and graphic design proposals, her reality checks with teen wording, and the full and final formatting of the work, transforming a simple word document to its present, professional format.

To these and all my other children, with love, whose support and persistent encouragement really kept me working. Thank you all.

Most of all, I thank my husband, my soul mate, for being the rock upon which I lean, who listened to my thoughts, consoled me when things got tough, revitalized me when my energies flagged, and continues to support, advise, and be my other half. Thank you for being accepting and tolerant of all the late nights, not-quite-vacations and time spent totally absorbed in this project.

From Us Both

We give thanks to Hashem Yisboroch for granting us the privilege, aptitude and time to bring this work to fruition, and sending us talented helpers along the way.

Thank you to Mrs. Sara Itzkowitz and Mrs. Talya Turk, from Bnos Yisroel of Baltimore for their invaluable input.

Thank you to the very talented Shoshana Radunsky for the beautiful jacket design. Your patience in working with our many proposals, revisions and delays, and your tolerance while we traversed the learning curve to understand just what we needed to provide was awesome and deeply appreciated.

Thanks to Rivky Schwebel for your excellent editing amongst all your other work. It was a pleasure working with you! Thanks to MindiMeira Blaxberg for zeroing in on the edits everyone else missed. You are a pleasure to work with.

A special thank you to Shulamis Tova Storch for her continued support, enthusiasm and suggestions, as well as her enterprising efforts to select the best cover. The selection of this cover, from amongst many, is due to her perseverance in obtaining feedback from teens about the most-liked cover design.

We are very grateful to *Binyan* magazine and the *Baltimore Jewish Times*, where many of these stories appeared in their earlier versions. Thank you to outstanding editors Mrs. Chavi Ernster, Mrs. Rachel Hubner, Mrs. Shira Moncharsh, Mrs. Maayan Jaffee, and Mr. Joshua Runyan.

Haskomos

May Hashem continue to bless our rebbaim, our gedolei hador, with the understanding and wisdom to guide us.

The Center for Jewish Family Life/
Project YES
56 Briarcliff Drive
Monsey, NY 10952-5552

10 Tammuz 5777

It is my pleasure to recommend, "Step into My Shoes," an excellent book by Danielle Sarah Storch and Tova NessAiver which teaches tweens and teens about the Torah values as they relate to social interactions with their peers and family members.

It is easy to codify the halachic requirements for a kosher lulav and esrog, but far more complicated to explain and clarify the timeless guidance of our sages that govern day-to-day behavior.

When reviewing a draft of the book, I was impressed by:

- The reflective nature of the lessons, where the kids are encouraged to step back and examine their everyday interactions by walking them through various scenarios
- The way the Torah values were presented in a way that is not "preachy"
- How children were not made to feel inadequate or worse for not having the "right" responses to social dilemmas, but rather to look at their middos as a work in progress

I wish the authors great success with their project and hope that this will be the first of many works they will produce and release.

Rabbi Yakov Horowitz

Dean Yeshiva Darchei Noam, Monsey
Founder and Director Project Y.E.S

מאיר אלטר הלוי הורוויץ
בן לכ״ק מרן אאמו״ר מבוסטון זצללה״ה זיע״א
עיה״ק ירושלים תובב״א
The Bostoner Rebbe of Yerushalayim

ב״ה

ו' טבת תשע״ז

I have reviewed the sample version of "Step Into *My* Shoes," an educational workbook for pre-teens and teens to be introduced to how Torah values interact with their every day struggles. Personally interacting with many young people myself and knowing the problems and questions that teens confront as they mature, both those who 'follow the crowd' and are influenced by peer pressure, as well as those who are intellectually curious and wish to express themselves as an individual, this book undertakes implanting a Torah perspective to interpersonal relationships.

I believe that this publication will assist educators to be able to impart Middos Tovos and a positive outlook on life to the young adults they are entrusted with that will help them through these difficult years and successfully reach the next stages in their lives. I found that this book addresses issues which are not generally covered in the curriculum of most schools and should be a welcome addition to the resources available to Rabbis, teachers and youth leaders.

May this book succeed in its most worthy undertaking, to spread Torah ideas and values to the many educators and their students.

With Torah Greetings from Jerusalem

[Rabbi Naftali Yehuda Halevi Horowitz]

מעלות האדמו״ר מבוסטון זצ״ל 1, ת.ד. 43033, הר נוף, ירושלים 91430
Tel/Fax: 972-2-651-9688 :טל/פקס * E-mail: 6519688@gmail.com

Shearith Israel Congregation
ק״ק שארית ישראל
PARK HEIGHTS AND GLEN AVENUES
BALTIMORE, MARYLAND 21215

YAAKOV HOPFER, RABBI
466-3060 Study
358-8281 Residence

יעקב האפפער
באלטימאר, מד.

[illegible] תשע״ו

In today's world it is increasingly difficult to reach teens and inspire them to incorporate Torah values in their everyday interactions. Even when they have grown up in frum homes, the day-to-day behaviors they exhibit often do not reflect that they have truly grasped and internalized the precepts of ahavas Hashem, ahavas Habriyos, & the need to build strong charachter.

With captivating stories that model rather than preach, Step into My Shoes skillfully provides a pleasurable way for teens to absorb and implement Torah directed behavior. It provides a template for educators & parents as well, showing how healthy interactions take place within the fold of our mesorah.

Interacting with teens on a regular basis, I believe these stories may strongly impact their thinking & behavior, helping them to view others through the lens of kindness and compassion, and become more sensitive to the way their behavior affects others.

Shearith Israel Congregation
ק״ק שארית ישראל
PARK HEIGHTS AND GLEN AVENUES
BALTIMORE, MARYLAND 21215

YAKOV HOPFER, RABBI
466-3060 Study
358-8281 Residence

יעקב האפפער
באלטימאר, מד.

It will be a valuable addition to any curriculum and a wonderful resource for jump starting Shabbos table discussions.

For any endevor to be successful it needs heavenly help. For a sefer kadosh to be a success it needs an additional component, the author must personally represent the ideas that he is trying to convey. Mrs Tova Ress Rivel and Mrs Danielle Sarah Storch are both women of sterling middos whose desire is to greatly enhance kavod shamayim

Wishing you great success!

With great admiration and respect

Yaakov Hopfer

Shearith Israel Congregation
ק״ק שארית ישראל
PARK HEIGHTS AND GLEN AVENUES
BALTIMORE, MARYLAND 21215

מנחם אב תשע״ז

For easier reading, we have transcribed Rabbi Hopfer's haskomo to print:

In today's world it is increasingly difficult to reach teens and inspire them to incorporate Torah values in their everyday interactions. Even when they have grown up in frum homes, the day-to-day behavior they exhibit often does not reflect that they have truly grasped and internalized the precepts of ahavas Hamokom, ahavas Habriyos, and the need to build strong character.

With captivating stories that model rather than preach, *Step into My Shoes* skillfully provides a pleasurable way for teens to absorb and implement Torah directed behavior. It provides a template for educators and parents as well, showing how healthy interactions take place within the folds of our mesorah.

Interacting with teens on a regular basis, I believe these stories may strongly impact their thinking and behavior, helping them to view others through the lens of kindness and compassion, and become more sensitive to the way their behavior affects others.

It will be a valuable addition to any curriculum and a wonderful resource for jump-starting Shabbos table discussions.

For any endeavor to be successful it needs heavenly help. For a sefer kadosh to be a success it needs an additional component, the author must personally represent the ideas that he is trying to convey. Mrs. Tova NessAiver and Mrs. Danielle Sarah Storch are both women of sterling middos whose desire is to greatly enhance kavod shamayim.

Wishing you great success!

With great admiration and respect,
Yaakov Hopfer

It's All About Attitude

A rabbi was walking through the street with several of his students when they came upon the body of a dead dog. "What a disgusting smell," they remarked. "What beautiful white teeth it has," responded the rabbi. The students were then sorry that they had said something negative about the dead dog.

Why? Wasn't it true?

The rabbi was teaching his students that even when there is something obviously unpleasant or distasteful before us, we can and should still look for and find something positive. If we shouldn't speak negatively about a dead dog, how much more so should we be careful to speak in positive ways about other human beings.

("Duties of the Heart" by Rabbi Bachya Ibn Pekudah)

The rabbi was teaching his students to develop the attitude and habit of seeing and speaking of the good in the world.

Yes, there is plenty of fault to find in things and people. But if we get into the habit of speaking of the good, it will become second nature, and we will be happier, more fulfilled people. If we get into the habit of speaking badly about things, then that will be our nature, and we will become discouraged and critical.

What does it take to train ourselves to see the positive in others?

We must learn to see things from another's perspective—step into their shoes—and realize that we are truly all Hashem's people, all trying to find our way and all there to help each other.

Let us work together to develop the right attitudes that align us with Hashem's path, the path of Torah ... come Step Into My Shoes.

In the merit of our seeking the good in others, may G-d only seek the good in us.